It's another great book from CGP...

This book covers the **Edexcel Level 1/Level 2 in Chemistry** and the **Edexcel International GCSE in Chemistry**.

It's also great for the Edexcel International GCSE in **Science (Double Award)** — but you won't need to learn the Paper 2 material if you're doing this course.

We've even included a free Online Edition so that you can revise on a computer or tablet — wherever you are.

How to get your free Online Edition

Just go to **cgpbooks.co.uk/extras** and enter this code...

2293 6467 6123 5762

By the way, this code only works for one person. If somebody else has used this book before you, they might have already claimed the Online Edition.

CGP — still the best! ☺

Our sole aim here at CGP is to produce the highest quality books — carefully written, immaculately presented and dangerously close to being funny.

Then we work our socks off to get them out to you — at the cheapest possible prices.

Contents

This book covers both **Chemistry Paper 1** and **Chemistry Paper 2** material. Some material is needed for **Paper 2 only**
— we've clearly marked this in green boxes.

The Paper 2 questions in the book are also printed in green.

If you're doing a **Science (Double Award)** qualification
you **don't** need to learn the Paper 2 material.

Paper 2

Paper 2

Published by CGP

From original material by Paddy Gannon.

Editors:
Katie Braid, Katherine Craig, Mary Falkner, Christopher Lindle,
Helen Ronan and Hayley Thompson.

Contributors:
Mike Thompson

ISBN: 978 1 84762 692 9

With thanks to Chris Elliss, Rosie McCurrie and Glenn Rogers for the proofreading.
With thanks to Jonathan Schofield for the external review.
With thanks to Anna Lupton for the copyright research.

With thanks to iStockphoto for permission to reproduce the photo on page 38.

Graph to show trend in atmospheric CO_2 concentration and global temperature on page 40
based on data by EPICA Community Members 2004 and Siegenthaler et al 2005.

Printed by Elanders Ltd, Newcastle upon Tyne.
Clipart from Corel®

Based on the classic CGP style created by Richard Parsons.

Text, design, layout and original illustrations © Coordination Group Publications Ltd. (CGP) 2012
All rights reserved.

Photocopying more than one chapter of this book is not permitted. Extra copies are available from CGP.
0800 1712 712 • www.cgpbooks.co.uk

States of Matter

You can explain quite a bit of the stuff in Chemistry if you can get your head round this lot.

The Three States of Matter — Solid, Liquid and Gas

Materials come in <u>three</u> different forms — <u>solid</u>, <u>liquid</u> and <u>gas</u>. These are the <u>Three States of Matter</u>. Which <u>state</u> you get (<u>solid</u>, <u>liquid</u> or <u>gas</u>) depends on how <u>strong</u> the forces of attraction are between the particles of the material. How strong the forces are depends on <u>THREE THINGS</u>:

    a) the <u>material</u>   b) the <u>temperature</u>   c) the <u>pressure</u>.

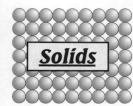

Solids

1) In solids, there are <u>strong forces</u> of attraction between particles, which holds them <u>close together</u> in <u>fixed positions</u> to form a very regular <u>lattice arrangement</u>.

2) The particles <u>don't move</u> from their positions, so all solids keep a <u>definite shape</u> and <u>volume</u>, and don't flow like liquids.

3) The particles <u>vibrate</u> about their positions — the <u>hotter</u> the solid becomes, the <u>more</u> they vibrate (causing solids to <u>expand</u> slightly when heated).

Liquids

1) In liquids, there is a <u>weak force</u> of attraction between the particles. They're randomly arranged and <u>free</u> to <u>move</u> past each other, but they tend to <u>stick closely together</u>.

2) Liquids have a definite volume but <u>don't</u> keep a <u>definite shape</u>, and will flow to fill the bottom of a container.

3) The particles are <u>constantly</u> moving with <u>random motion</u>. The <u>hotter</u> the liquid gets, the <u>faster</u> they move. This causes liquids to <u>expand</u> slightly when heated.

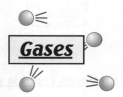

Gases

1) In gases, the force of attraction between the particles is <u>very weak</u> — they're <u>free</u> to <u>move</u> and are <u>far apart</u>. The particles in gases travel in <u>straight lines</u>.

2) Gases <u>don't</u> keep a definite <u>shape</u> or <u>volume</u> and will always <u>fill</u> any container.

3) The particles move <u>constantly</u> with <u>random motion</u>. The <u>hotter</u> the gas gets, the <u>faster</u> they move. Gases either <u>expand</u> when heated, or their <u>pressure increases</u>.

Substances Can Change from One State to Another

<u>Physical changes</u> don't change the particles — just their <u>arrangement</u> or their <u>energy</u>.

3) At a <u>certain temperature</u>, the particles have enough energy to <u>break free</u> from their positions. This is called <u>MELTING</u> and the <u>solid</u> turns into a <u>liquid</u>.

4) When a liquid is <u>heated</u>, again the particles get even <u>more</u> energy.

2) This makes the particles vibrate <u>more</u>, which <u>weakens</u> the <u>forces</u> that hold the solid together. This makes the solid <u>expand</u>.

1) When a solid is <u>heated</u>, its particles gain more <u>energy</u>.

5) This energy makes the particles move <u>faster</u>, which <u>weakens</u> and <u>breaks</u> the bonds holding the liquid together.

6) At a <u>certain temperature</u>, the particles have <u>enough</u> energy to <u>break</u> their bonds. This is called <u>EVAPORATING</u> and the <u>liquid</u> turns into a <u>gas</u>.

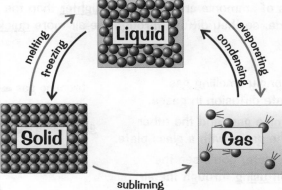

A Red Arrow means heat energy is supplied

A Blue Arrow means heat energy is given out

Phew, what a page — particle-ularly gripping stuff...

think it's pretty clever the way you can explain all the differences between solids, liquids and gases with just page full of blue and pink snooker balls. Anyway, that's the easy bit. The not-so-easy bit is learning it all.

Movement of Particles

There are many nifty experiments that you can do to observe the wonders of chemistry. Here are a few...

Diffusion <u>is the</u> Movement of Particles <u>Through a</u> Liquid <u>or</u> Gas

<u>Diffusion</u> is the <u>gradual movement</u> of particles from places where there are <u>lots</u> of them to places where there are <u>fewer</u> of them. It's just the <u>natural tendency</u> for stuff to <u>spread out</u>. You can use the experiment below to demonstrate diffusion...

Potassium Manganate(VII) and Water

<u>Potassium manganate(VII)</u> is great for this experiment because it's <u>bright purple</u>.

1) If you take a beaker of <u>water</u> and place some potassium manganate(VII) at the bottom, the purple colour <u>slowly spreads</u> out to fill the beaker.

2) This is chemistry in action (groan)... The particles of potassium manganate(VII) are <u>diffusing</u> out among the particles of water.

3) It's the <u>random motion</u> of particles in a liquid (see the previous page) that causes the purple colour to eventually be <u>evenly spread out</u> throughout the water.

> **Potassium Manganate(VII) solution can be diluted by adding water**
>
> If you were to <u>add more water</u> to the final purple solution, the potassium manganate(VII) particles would <u>spread even further apart</u> and the solution would be <u>less purple</u>. This is called <u>dilution</u>.

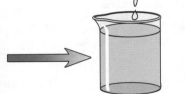

Ammonia and Hydrogen Chloride

1) Aqueous ammonia (NH_3) gives off <u>ammonia gas</u>. Hydrochloric acid (HCl) gives off <u>hydrogen chloride gas</u>.

2) If you set up an experiment like this...

glass tube

cotton wool soaked in hydrochloric acid

cotton wool soaked in aqueous ammonia

ring of ammonium chloride

...you'll get a <u>white ring</u> of <u>ammonium chloride</u> forming in the glass tube.

3) The NH_3 gas <u>diffuses</u> from one end of the tube and the HCl gas <u>diffuses</u> from the other. When they meet they <u>react</u> to form ammonium chloride.

4) The ring doesn't form exactly in the middle of the glass tube — it forms nearest the end of the tube where the <u>hydrochloric acid</u> was.

5) This is because the particles of ammonia are <u>smaller</u> and <u>lighter</u> than the particles of hydrogen chloride, so they diffuse through the air more <u>quickly</u>.

Bromine Gas and Air

1) Bromine gas is a <u>brown</u>, strongly smelling gas. You can use it to demonstrate diffusion in gases.

2) Fill half a <u>gas jar</u> full of <u>bromine gas</u>, and the other half full of air — separate the gases with a glass plate.

3) When you <u>remove</u> the glass plate, you'll see the brown bromine gas <u>slowly diffusing</u> through the air.

4) The <u>random motion</u> of the particles means that the bromine will eventually diffuse right through the air.

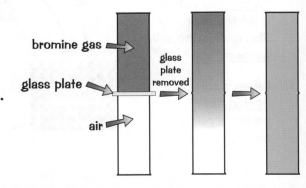

bromine gas

glass plate removed

glass plate

air

Sleeping on the book doesn't make the words diffuse into your head...

If you're lucky, you might get to see these experiments in the lab. Or, your teacher might show you some equally exciting but different experiments to demonstrate <u>diffusion of particles</u>. Either way, you've gotta learn it.

Atoms

All substances are made up of <u>atoms</u>. There are quite a few <u>different models</u> of the atom — but chemists tend to like this <u>nuclear model</u> best.

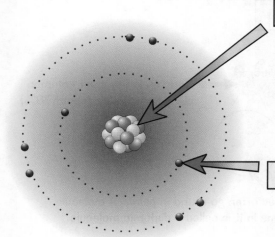

The Nucleus

1) It's in the <u>middle</u> of the atom.
2) It contains <u>protons</u> and <u>neutrons</u>.
3) It has a <u>positive charge</u> because of the protons.
4) Almost the <u>whole</u> mass of the atom is <u>concentrated</u> in the nucleus.
5) But size-wise it's <u>tiny</u> compared to the rest of the atom.

There's more on electron shells on page 9.

The Electrons

1) They move <u>around</u> the nucleus in energy levels called shells.
2) They're <u>negatively charged</u>.
3) They're <u>tiny</u>, but they cover <u>a lot of space</u>.
4) The <u>size</u> of their orbits determines how big the atom is.
5) They have virtually <u>no</u> mass.

<u>Protons</u> are <u>heavy</u> and <u>positively charged</u>.
<u>Neutrons</u> are <u>heavy</u> and <u>neutral</u>.
<u>Electrons</u> are <u>tiny</u> and <u>negatively charged</u>. (Electron mass is often taken as <u>zero</u>.)

PARTICLE	RELATIVE MASS	RELATIVE CHARGE
Proton	1	+1
Neutron	1	0
Electron	$\frac{1}{2000}$	−1

Number of Electrons Equals Number of Protons

1) Neutral atoms have <u>no charge</u> overall.
2) The <u>charge</u> on the electrons is the <u>same</u> size as the charge on the <u>protons</u> — but <u>opposite</u>.
3) This means the <u>number</u> of <u>electrons</u> always equals the <u>number</u> of <u>protons</u> in a <u>neutral atom</u>.
4) If some electrons are <u>added or removed</u>, the atom becomes <u>charged</u> and is then an <u>ion</u>.

Atomic Number and Mass Number Describe an Atom

These two numbers tell you how many of each kind of particle an atom has.

The Mass Number — Total of protons and neutrons

The Atomic Number — Number of protons

23
Na
11

1) The <u>atomic number</u> tells you how many <u>protons</u> there are.
2) Atoms of the <u>same</u> element all have the <u>same</u> number of <u>protons</u> — so atoms of <u>different</u> elements will have <u>different</u> numbers of <u>protons</u>.
3) To get the number of <u>neutrons</u>, just <u>subtract</u> the <u>atomic number</u> from the <u>mass number</u>.

Molecules are Groups of Atoms

1) Atoms can join together to form <u>molecules</u>.
2) Some molecules are made from just <u>one element</u> (e.g. H_2, N_2), while others are made up of <u>more than one element</u> (e.g. H_2O, CO_2).
3) Molecules are held together by <u>covalent bonds</u> (there's more on bonds on pages 10-13).

Number of electrons = number of protons...

This stuff might seem a bit useless at first, but it should be permanently engraved into your mind. If you don't know these basic facts, you've got no chance of understanding the rest of Chemistry. So <u>learn it now</u>, and watch as the Universe unfolds and reveals its timeless mysteries to you...

Elements, Compounds and Mixtures

There are only about 100 or so different kinds of atoms, which doesn't sound too bad.
But they can join together in loads of different combinations, which makes life more complicated.

Elements Consist of One Type of Atom Only

Quite a lot of everyday substances are elements:

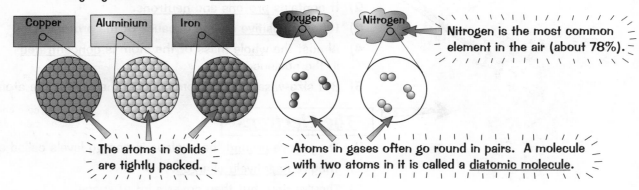

Nitrogen is the most common element in the air (about 78%).

The atoms in solids are tightly packed.

Atoms in gases often go round in pairs. A molecule with two atoms in it is called a diatomic molecule.

Compounds are Chemically Bonded

carbon + oxygen ⟶ carbon dioxide

1) A compound is a substance that is made of two or more different elements which are chemically joined (bonded) together.

2) For example, carbon dioxide is a compound formed from a chemical reaction. One carbon atom reacts with two oxygen atoms to form a molecule of carbon dioxide, with the formula CO_2.

3) It's very difficult to separate the two original elements out again.

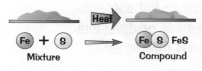

Mixture ⟶ Compound

4) The properties of a compound are often totally different from the properties of the original elements.

5) For example, if a mixture of iron and sulphur is heated, the iron and sulphur atoms react to form the compound iron sulphide (FeS). Iron sulphide is not much like iron (e.g. it's not attracted to a magnet), nor is it much like sulphur (e.g. it's not yellow in colour).

Mixtures are Easily Separated — Not Like Compounds

1) Unlike in a compound, there's no chemical bond between the different parts of a mixture. The parts can be separated out by physical methods such as distillation (see page 7).

2) Air is a mixture of gases, mainly nitrogen, oxygen, carbon dioxide and argon. The gases can all be separated out fairly easily.

3) The properties of a mixture are just a mixture of the properties of the separate parts.

4) A mixture of iron powder and sulphur powder will show the properties of both iron and sulphur. It will contain grey magnetic bits of iron and bright yellow bits of sulphur.

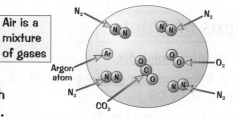

Air is a mixture of gases

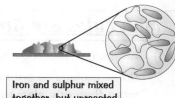

Iron and sulphur mixed together, but unreacted.

5) Crude oil is a mixture of different length hydrocarbon molecules — see page 70.

Not learning this stuff will only compound your problems...

Mixtures and compounds. To most people they sound like basically the same thing. Not to examiners, I'm afraid. If you understand the difference between the mixture of iron powder and sulphur powder, and the compound iron sulphide, it'll make all this stuff easier to remember.

Filtration and Crystallisation

Remember, the components of mixtures are <u>not</u> chemically joined (see page 4).
This means you can <u>separate</u> them <u>very easily</u> using <u>physical methods</u>.

Filtration <u>is Used to Separate an</u> Insoluble Solid <u>from a</u> Liquid

1) Filtration can be used if your <u>product</u> is an <u>insoluble solid</u> that needs to be separated from a <u>liquid reaction mixture</u>.

2) It can be used in <u>purification</u> as well. For example, <u>solid impurities</u> in the reaction mixture can be separated out using <u>filtration</u>.

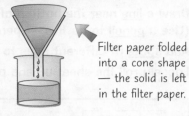

Filter paper folded into a cone shape — the solid is left in the filter paper.

Crystallisation <u>is Used to Separate a</u> Soluble Solid <u>from a</u> Solution

1) Here's how you <u>crystallise</u> a product...
2) Pour the solution into an <u>evaporating dish</u>.
3) Slowly <u>heat</u> the solution. Some of the <u>solvent</u> will evaporate and the solution will get more <u>concentrated</u>. Stop heating when <u>crystals</u> start to form.
4) Remove the dish from the heat and leave it in a <u>warm place</u> for the rest of the solvent to slowly <u>evaporate</u> — this way you get nice <u>big crystals</u>.
5) Finally, you've got to <u>dry</u> the product — you can use a <u>drying oven</u> or a <u>desiccator</u> for this (a desiccator contains chemicals that remove water from the surroundings).

evaporating dish

<u>You Can Use</u> Filtration <u>and</u> Crystallisation <u>to Separate</u> Rock Salt

1) <u>Rock salt</u> is simply a <u>mixture</u> of <u>salt</u> and <u>sand</u> (they spread it on the roads in winter).
2) Salt and sand are both <u>compounds</u> — but <u>salt dissolves</u> in water and <u>sand doesn't</u>. This <u>vital difference</u> in their <u>physical properties</u> gives a great way to <u>separate</u> them.
3) You need to <u>learn the four steps</u> of the method:

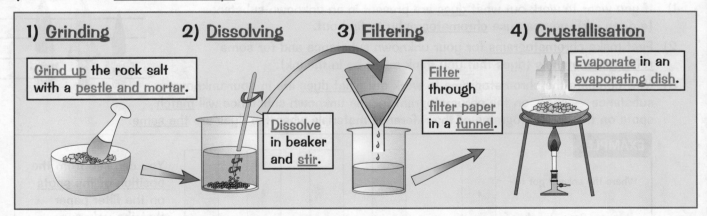

4) The sand doesn't dissolve (it's <u>insoluble</u>), so it stays as <u>big grains</u>. These <u>won't fit</u> through the <u>tiny holes</u> in the filter paper — so it <u>collects on the filter paper</u>.
5) The <u>salt</u> is dissolved in <u>solution</u>, so it does go through — and when the water's <u>evaporated</u>, the salt forms as <u>crystals</u> in the <u>evaporating dish</u>.

<u>Revise mixtures — just filter out the important bits...</u>

One page on separation down, and a couple more to come. But hold your horses... Before you dash on to the next page (I know, I know, it's just so exciting), make sure you've learnt all the details on this page first. The next page will still be there when you're done. Now repeat after me. Grind, dissolve, filter, crystallise...

Chromatography

Chromatography is another method used by chemists to separate out mixtures. You can use paper chromatography to separate out dyes — e.g. in inks, paints, food colourings etc. It's, er, fascinating stuff.

You Need to Know How to Do Paper Chromatography

1) Draw a line near the bottom of a sheet of filter paper.
   (Use a pencil to do this — pencil marks are insoluble and won't react with the solvent.)
2) Add spots of different dyes to the line at regular intervals.
3) Loosely roll the sheet up and put it in a beaker of solvent, e.g. water.

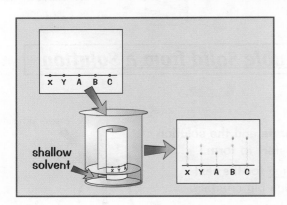

shallow solvent

4) The solvent used depends on what's being tested. Some compounds dissolve well in water, but sometimes other solvents, like ethanol, are needed.
5) Make sure the dyes aren't touching the solvent — you don't want them to dissolve into it.
6) Place a lid on top of the container to stop the solvent evaporating.
7) The solvent seeps up the paper, carrying the dyes with it.
8) Each different dye will move up the paper at a different rate and form a spot in a different place.
9) The end result is a pattern of spots called a chromatogram

How Chromatography Separates Mixtures...

1) Chromatography works because different dyes will move up the paper at different rates.
2) Some will stick to the paper and others will dissolve more readily in the solvent and travel more quickly.
3) The distance the dyes travel up the paper depends on the solvent and the paper you use.

Chromatography Can Help You to Identify Dyes

1) If you want to work out what dyes are present in an unknown substance (e.g. an ink), you can use chromatography to find out.
2) First make chromatograms for your unknown substance and for some reference materials (dyes that you think might be in the ink).
3) Now compare the chromatograms to work out what dyes are in your unknown substance — spots on the chromatogram for the unknown substance will match spots on the chromatograms of the reference materials when the dyes are the same.

EXAMPLE:

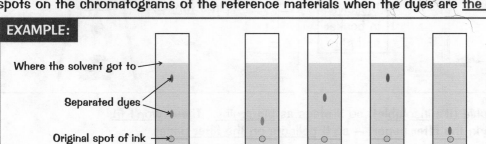

Where the solvent got to

Separated dyes

Original spot of ink

Unknown ink   Dye A   Dye B   Dye C   Dye D

You can see from the position of the spots on the filter paper that the unknown ink contains dye A and dye C.

Comb-atography — identifies mysterious things in your hair...

So that's chromatography — it's pretty neat once you get your head around it. You can use it for all kinds of things, like crime-fighting... CSIs use chromatography to identify unknown substances from crime scenes. They can even use it to identify inks used to print forged money and link 'em back to a suspect. Ain't science grand.

Distillation

Distillation is used to separate mixtures that contain <u>liquids</u>.
There are two types that you need to know about — <u>simple</u> and <u>fractional</u>.

Simple Distillation *is Used to Separate Out Solutions*

1) <u>Simple distillation</u> is used for separating out a <u>liquid</u> from a <u>solution</u>.

2) The solution is <u>heated</u>. The part of the solution that has the lowest boiling point <u>evaporates</u>.

3) The <u>vapour</u> is then <u>cooled</u>, <u>condenses</u> (turns back into a liquid) and is <u>collected</u>.

4) The rest of the <u>solution</u> is left behind in the flask.

5) You can use simple distillation to get <u>pure water</u> from <u>seawater</u>. The <u>water</u> evaporates and is condensed and collected. Eventually you'll end up with just the <u>salt</u> left in the flask.

6) The <u>problem</u> with simple distillation is that you can only use it to separate things with <u>very different</u> boiling points.

7) If you have a <u>mixture of liquids</u> with <u>similar boiling points</u>, you need another method to separate them out — like fractional distillation...

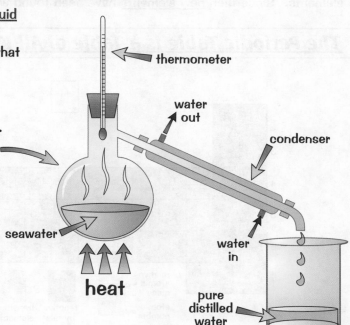

Fractional Distillation *is Used to Separate a Mixture of Liquids*

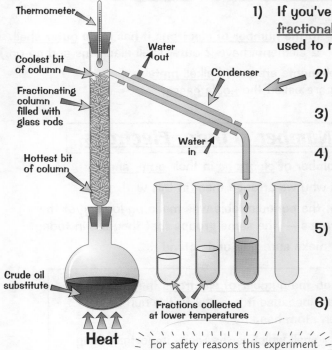

1) If you've got a <u>mixture of liquids</u> you can separate it using <u>fractional distillation</u>. Here is a lab demonstration that can be used to model <u>fractional distillation of crude oil</u> at a <u>refinery</u>.

2) You put your <u>mixture</u> in a flask and stick a <u>fractionating column</u> on top. Then you heat it.

3) The <u>different liquids</u> will all have <u>different boiling points</u> — so they will evaporate at <u>different temperatures</u>.

4) The liquid with the <u>lowest boiling point</u> evaporates first. When the temperature on the thermometer matches the boiling point of this liquid, it will reach the <u>top</u> of the column.

5) Liquids with <u>higher boiling points</u> might also start to evaporate. But the column is <u>cooler</u> towards the <u>top</u>. So they will only get part of the way up before <u>condensing</u> and running back down towards the flask.

6) When the first liquid has been collected, you <u>raise the temperature</u> until the <u>next one</u> reaches the top.

Fractionating — sounds a bit too much like maths to me...

Remember that parts of <u>mixtures aren't joined together</u> — so you can separate them by <u>physical methods</u> without the need for chemical reactions. And don't forget — you need to learn these separation techniques for the exam. In fact you'd be crazy not to — so make sure you can <u>scribble</u> all this stuff down. Enjoy.

The Periodic Table

In 1869, Dmitri Mendeleev arranged 50 known elements in order of atomic mass to make a Table of Elements. Mendeleev's table placed elements with similar chemical properties in the same vertical groups — but he found that he had to leave gaps in his table to make this work. The gaps in Mendeleev's table of elements were really clever because they predicted the properties of undiscovered elements. Since then new elements have been found which fit into the gaps left in Mendeleev's table...

The Periodic Table is a Table of All Known Elements

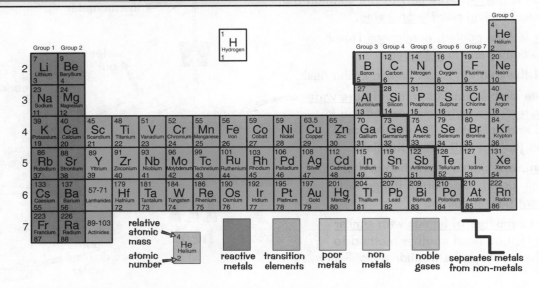

1) We now know there are 100ish elements that all materials are made of, with more still being 'discovered'.

2) The modern periodic table shows the elements in order of increasing atomic number.

3) The periodic table is laid out so that elements with similar properties form columns.

4) These vertical columns are called groups.

5) The group to which an element belongs corresponds to the number of electrons it has in its outer shell. (Group 1 elements have 1 outer shell electron, Group 2 elements have 2 outer shell electrons and so on.)

6) Some of the groups have special names. Group 1 elements are called alkali metals. Group 7 elements are called halogens, and Group 0 are called the noble gases.

Elements in a Group Have the Same Number of Outer Electrons

1) The elements in any one group all have the same number of electrons in their outer shell.

2) That's why they have similar properties. And that's why we arrange them in this way.

3) When only a small number of elements were known, the periodic table was made by looking at the properties of the elements and arranging them in groups — the same groups that they are in today.

4) This idea is extremely important to chemistry — so make sure you understand it.

> The properties of the elements depend on the number of electrons they have. Atomic number is therefore very significant because it is equal to the number of electrons each atom has.
>
> But it's the number of electrons in the outer shell which is the really important thing.

I've got a periodic table — Queen Anne legs and everything...

Physicists can produce new elements in particle accelerators, but they're all radioactive. Most of them only last a fraction of a second before they decay. Most haven't even got proper names yet, just temporary names made by writing their atomic numbers in Latin. But then "element 118" sounds pretty cool in Latin — ununoctium...

Electron Shells

The fact that electrons occupy "shells" around the nucleus is what causes the whole of chemistry.
Remember that, and watch how it applies to each bit of it. It's ace.

Electron Shell Rules:

1) Electrons always occupy <u>shells</u> (sometimes called <u>energy levels</u>).
2) The <u>lowest</u> energy levels are <u>always filled first</u> — these are the ones closest to the nucleus.
3) Only <u>a certain number</u> of electrons are allowed in each shell:
   <u>1st shell:</u> 2   <u>2nd Shell:</u> 8   <u>3rd Shell:</u> 8
4) Atoms are much <u>happier</u> when they have <u>full electron shells</u> — like the <u>noble gases</u> in <u>Group 0</u>.
5) In most atoms the <u>outer shell</u> is <u>not full</u> and this makes the atom want to <u>react</u>.

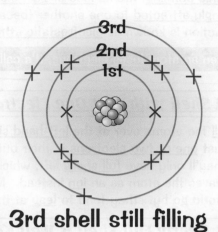

3rd shell still filling

Follow the Rules to Work Out Electronic Configurations

You need to know the <u>electronic configurations</u> for the first <u>20</u> elements (things get a bit more complicated after that). But they're not hard to work out. For a quick example, take nitrogen. <u>Follow these steps...</u>

1) The periodic table tells us nitrogen has <u>seven</u> protons... so it must have <u>seven</u> electrons.
2) Follow the '<u>Electron Shell Rules</u>' above. The <u>first</u> shell can only take 2 electrons and the <u>second</u> shell can take a <u>maximum</u> of 8 electrons.
3) So the electronic configuration for nitrogen <u>must</u> be <u>2, 5</u>. Easy peasy.
4) Now find the electronic configuration of <u>argon</u> (answer below).

The periodic table has a big gap here where the transition metals fit in on row four.

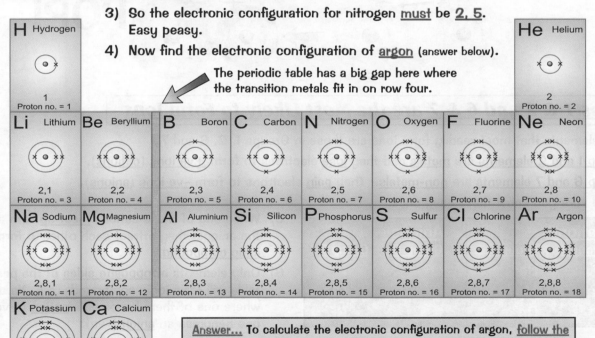

Answer... To calculate the electronic configuration of argon, <u>follow the electron shell rules</u>. It's got 18 protons, so it <u>must</u> have 18 electrons. The first shell must have <u>2</u> electrons, the second shell must have <u>8</u>, and so the third shell must have <u>8</u> as well. It's as easy as <u>2, 8, 8</u>.

One little duck and two fat ladies — 2, 8, 8...

You need to know enough about electron shells to draw out that <u>whole diagram</u> at the bottom of the page without looking at it. Obviously, you don't have to learn each element separately, just <u>learn the rules</u>. Cover the page: using a periodic table, find the atom with the electronic configuration 2, 8, 6.

Ionic Bonding

Ionic Bonding — Transfer of Electrons

In ionic bonding, atoms lose or gain electrons to form charged particles (called ions) which are then strongly attracted to one another (because of the attraction of opposite charges, + and −). This strong attraction is known as electrostatic attraction — it gives ionic compounds their high melting and boiling points.

When an atom loses electrons, it's called OXIDATION. When an atom gains electrons, it's called REDUCTION.

A Shell with Just One Electron is Well Keen to Get Rid...

All the atoms over at the left-hand side of the periodic table, e.g. sodium, potassium, calcium etc., have just one or two electrons in their outer shell. They're pretty keen to get shot of them, because then they'll only have full shells left, which is how they like it. So given half a chance they do get rid, and that leaves the atom as an ion instead. Now, ions aren't the kind of things that sit around quietly watching the world go by. They tend to leap at the first passing ion with an opposite charge and stick to it like glue.

A Nearly Full Shell is Well Keen to Get That Extra Electron...

On the other side of the periodic table, the elements in Group 6 and Group 7, such as oxygen and chlorine, have outer shells which are nearly full. They're obviously pretty keen to gain that extra one or two electrons to fill the shell up. When they do of course they become ions (you know, not the kind of things to sit around) and before you know it they've latched on to the atom (ion) that gave up the electron a moment earlier. The reaction of sodium and chlorine is a classic case:

The sodium atom gives up its outer electron and becomes an Na⁺ ion.

The chlorine atom picks up the spare electron and becomes a Cl⁻ ion.

Groups 1 & 2 and 6 & 7 are the Most Likely to Form Ions

1) The elements that most readily form ions are those in Groups 1, 2, 6 and 7.

2) Group 1 and 2 elements are metals and they lose electrons to form +ve ions (cations).

3) Group 6 and 7 elements are non-metals. They gain electrons to form −ve ions (anions).

4) Make sure you know these easy ones:

Cations		Anions	
Group 1	Group 2	Group 6	Group 7
Li⁺	Be²⁺	O²⁻	F⁻
Na⁺	Mg²⁺	S²⁻	Cl⁻
K⁺	Ca²⁺		Br⁻

5) When any of these cations meet up with any of the anions, they attract each other to form an ionic compound.

6) Only elements at opposite sides of the periodic table will form ionic compounds, e.g. Na and Cl, where one of them becomes a cation (+ve) and one becomes an anion (−ve).

7) You don't have to remember what ions most elements form — nope, you just look at the periodic table.

8) Elements in the same group all have the same number of outer electrons. So they have to lose or gain the same number to get a full outer shell. And this means that they form ions with the same charges.

Any old ion, any old ion — any, any, any old ion...

Remember, the + and − charges here are telling you what type of ion the atom will form in a chemical reaction. For example, sodium metal is made up of neutral sodium atoms (Na). They will only become sodium ions (Na⁺) if the sodium metal reacts with something — like water or chlorine.

Ionic Compounds

Make sure you've really got your head around the idea of ionic bonding before you start on this page.

Ionic Compounds All Form in a Similar Way

'Dot and cross' diagrams show what happens to the electrons when ionic bonding happens:

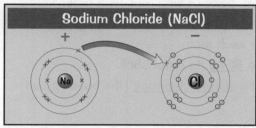

The sodium atom gives up its outer electron, becoming an Na+ ion. The chlorine atom picks up the electron, becoming a Cl- (chloride) ion.

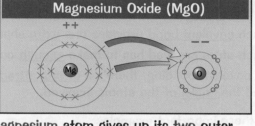

The magnesium atom gives up its two outer electrons, becoming an Mg^{2+} ion. The oxygen atom picks up the electrons, becoming an O^{2-} (oxide) ion.

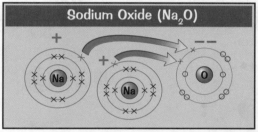

Two sodium atoms give up their outer electrons, becoming two Na+ ions. The oxygen atom picks up the two electrons, becoming an O^{2-} ion.

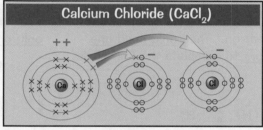

The calcium atom gives up its two outer electrons, becoming a Ca^{2+} ion. The two chlorine atoms pick up one electron each, becoming two Cl- (chloride) ions.

Notice that all the atoms end up with full outer shells as a result of this giving and taking of electrons.

Giant Ionic Structures Have High Melting and Boiling Points

1) Compounds with ionic bonding always have giant ionic structures.

2) The ions are held together in a closely packed 3D lattice arrangement by the attraction between oppositely charged ions.

3) The electrostatic attraction between oppositely charged ions is very strong. Because a lot of energy is needed to overcome the strong attraction, this means that ionic compounds have high melting and boiling points.

4) The charges on the ions in the lattice also affect the strength of the ionic bonding. A lattice of 2+ and 2- ions will be held together by stronger forces of attraction than a lattice of 1+ and 1- ions.

5) This means that lattices made up of higher charge ions will have higher melting and boiling points.

6) Sodium chloride has a typical ionic structure. You need to be able to draw its structure which can be represented like this:

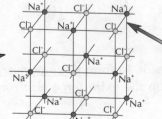

The Na+ and Cl- ions alternate.

Paper 2

Giant ionic lattices — all over your chips...

...I dare you to ask for that next time you're in the chippy. Anyway, make sure you know what's going on in a dot and cross diagram. Cover the page and practise drawing a few — it's the only way to get the hang of them.

Covalent Bonding

Ionic bonding (see page 10) isn't the only kind of bonding you need to know about — there's <u>covalent bonding</u> too. This is where atoms <u>share electrons</u> with each other so that they've got <u>full outer shells</u>.

A <u>Covalent</u> Bond is a <u>Shared Pair of Electrons</u>

1) Sometimes atoms prefer to make <u>covalent bonds</u> by <u>sharing</u> pairs of electrons with other atoms.
2) This way <u>both</u> atoms feel that they have a <u>full outer shell</u>, and that makes them happy.
3) Each <u>covalent bond</u> provides one <u>extra</u> shared electron for each atom.
4) Each atom involved has to make <u>enough</u> covalent bonds to <u>fill up</u> its outer shell.
5) In covalent bonding, there's a <u>strong attraction</u> between the <u>shared electrons</u> (the bonding pair) and the <u>nuclei</u> of the atoms involved.

<u>Learn</u> these <u>important examples</u>:

Hydrogen, H₂

Hydrogen atoms have just one electron. They <u>only need one more</u> to complete the first shell...

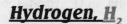

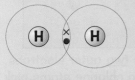

...so they often form <u>single covalent bonds</u> to achieve this.

Chlorine, Cl₂

...chlorine atoms also need <u>only one more</u> electron...

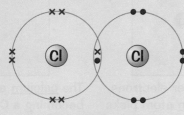

or Cl — Cl

Hydrogen Chloride, HCl

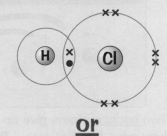

or

H — Cl

This is very similar to H₂ and Cl₂. Again, both atoms <u>only need one more electron</u> to complete their outer shells.

In a dot and cross diagram, you only have to draw the outer shell of electrons.

Ammonia, NH₃

Nitrogen has <u>five</u> outer electrons...

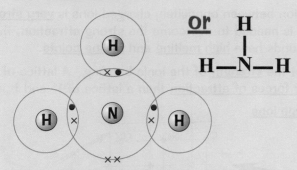

...so it needs to form <u>three covalent bonds</u> to make up the extra <u>three</u> electrons needed.

Nitrogen, N₂

Nitrogen atoms need <u>three more</u> electrons...

or N ≡ N

...so <u>two nitrogen atoms</u> share <u>three pairs of electrons</u> to fill their outer shells. This creates a <u>triple bond</u>.

<u>Covalent bonding — it's good to share...</u>

There's another page of covalent bonding diagrams to come, but make sure you can draw the <u>dot and cross diagrams</u> for the covalent compounds on this page first. When you've drawn a dot and cross diagram, it's a good idea to count up the number of electrons, just to <u>double-check</u> you've got <u>the right number</u> in the outer shell.

Covalent Bonding

Oxygen atoms have <u>six</u> outer electrons and need <u>two more</u> to complete their outer shell.

Water, H_2O

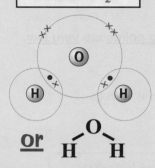

or

In <u>water molecules</u>, the oxygen shares a pair of electrons with two H atoms to form two <u>single covalent bonds</u>.

Oxygen, O_2

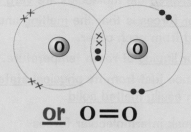

or O=O

In <u>oxygen gas</u> one oxygen atom shares two pairs of electrons with another to form a <u>double covalent bond</u>.

Carbon Dioxide, CO_2

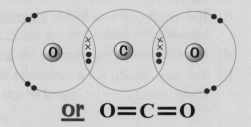

or O=C=O

In <u>carbon dioxide</u> two oxygen atoms share two pairs of electrons with a carbon atom to form <u>two double covalent bonds</u>.

Methane, CH_4

Carbon has <u>four outer electrons</u>, which is <u>half a full</u> shell.

or

It forms <u>four covalent bonds</u> with <u>hydrogen</u> atoms to fill up its outer shell.

Ethane, C_2H_6

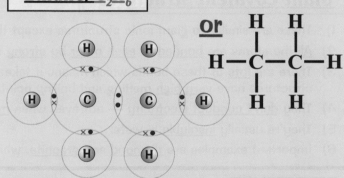

In <u>ethane</u>, 6 <u>hydrogen</u> atoms each share their only electron with one of two carbon atoms. The two carbon atoms then share their last electrons with <u>each other</u> in a <u>single covalent bond</u>.

Ethene, C_2H_4

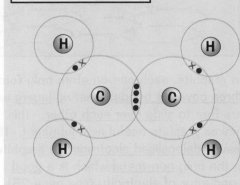

or

In <u>ethene</u>, 4 hydrogen atoms each share their only electron with one of two carbon atoms. The two carbon atoms then share their last <u>two</u> electrons with each other to form a <u>carbon-carbon double bond</u>.

Double bonds — now that's just being greedy...

Every atom wants a full outer shell, and they can get that either by becoming an ion (see page 11) or by sharing electrons. Once you understand that, you should be able to apply it to any example they give you in the exam.

Covalent Substances

Substances containing <u>covalent bonds</u> can be <u>simple molecules</u> or <u>giant structures</u>.

Simple Molecular Substances

1) The atoms <u>within a molecule</u> are held together by <u>very strong</u> covalent bonds.

2) By contrast, the forces of attraction <u>between</u> the molecules are <u>very weak</u>.

3) The result of these feeble <u>intermolecular forces</u> is that the <u>melting</u> and <u>boiling points</u> are <u>very low</u>, because the molecules are <u>easily parted</u> from each other.

4) Most molecular substances are <u>gases or liquids</u> at room temperature.

5) You can usually tell a molecular substance just from its <u>physical state</u>, which is always kinda '<u>mushy</u>' — i.e. <u>liquid</u> or <u>gas</u> or an <u>easily melted solid</u>.

Very weak intermolecular forces

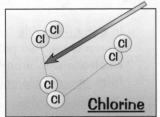

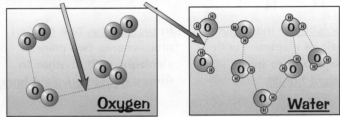

Chlorine Oxygen Water

Giant Covalent Structures

1) These are similar to giant ionic structures except that there are <u>no charged ions</u>.

2) <u>All</u> the atoms are <u>bonded</u> to <u>each other</u> by <u>strong</u> covalent bonds.

3) There are <u>lots</u> of these bonds which means it takes a <u>lot of energy</u> to break them, so giant covalent structures have <u>very high</u> melting and boiling points.

4) They <u>don't conduct electricity</u> — not even when <u>molten</u> (except for graphite that is — see below).

5) They're usually <u>insoluble</u> in water.

6) Important examples are <u>diamond</u> and <u>graphite</u>, which are both made only from <u>carbon atoms</u>.

Diamond

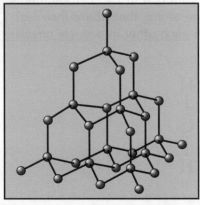

You need to be able to draw these structures.

Graphite

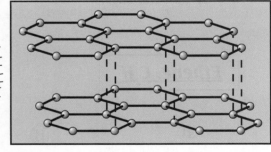

In diamond, each carbon atom forms <u>four covalent bonds</u> in a <u>very rigid</u> giant covalent structure. This structure makes diamond the <u>hardest</u> natural substance, so it's used for drill tips and cutting tools. And it's all <u>pretty</u> and <u>sparkly</u> too.

In graphite, each carbon atom only forms <u>three covalent bonds</u>, creating <u>layers</u> which are free to <u>slide over each other</u>. This makes graphite useful as a <u>lubricant</u>. It also leaves <u>delocalised electrons</u>, so graphite is the only <u>non-metal</u> which is a <u>good conductor of electricity</u> (see page 25).

Carbon is a girl's best friend...

The <u>two different types</u> of covalent substance are very different. Make sure you know about them both.

Paper 2

Paper 2

Revision Summary for Section 1 — 1

These certainly aren't the easiest questions you're going to come across. That's because they test what you know without giving you any clues. At first you might think they're impossibly difficult. Eventually you'll realise that they simply test whether you've learnt the stuff or not.

If you're struggling to answer these then you need to do some serious learning.

1) A substance keeps the same volume, but changes its shape according to the container it's in. Is it a solid, a liquid or a gas?

2) Are the forces of attraction between the particles in a liquid stronger or weaker than those in a gas?

3) Describe what happens when a substance changes from a liquid to a gas.

4) What is diffusion?

5) Describe an experiment that you can do to demonstrate diffusion.

6) Sketch the nuclear model of an atom. Give three details about the nucleus and three details about the electrons.

7) Draw a table showing the relative masses and charges of the three types of particle in an atom.

8) What do the mass number and atomic number of an element tell you?

9) Describe the difference between a mixture and a compound.

10)* Say which of the diagrams on the right shows: a) a mixture of compounds,

                                                    b) a mixture of elements,

                                                    c) an element,

                                                    d) a compound.

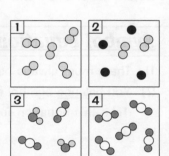

11)* Name the physical method you could use to separate these mixtures:

a) a soluble solid dissolved in water.

b) a mixture of liquids with different boiling points.

c) an insoluble solid mixed with a liquid.

12) Describe how you could separate the dyes in some inks using paper chromatography.

13) What feature of atoms determines the order of the modern periodic table?

14) How many electrons are in the outer shell of an atom of a Group 7 element?

15) Describe how you would work out the electron configuration of an atom, given its atomic number.

16)* Write out the electron configuration of potassium. (Use the periodic table on page 8 to help.)

17) Describe the process of ionic bonding.

18) Draw a dot and cross diagram to show the bonding in sodium chloride (NaCl).

19) What effect does the charge on the ions have on the melting point of an ionic compound?

20) What is covalent bonding?

21) Sketch dot and cross diagrams showing the bonding in molecules of:

a) hydrogen,   b) hydrogen chloride,   c) water,   d) carbon dioxide,   e) ethene.

22) a) Describe one property of simple molecular substances.

b) Explain how the bonding in simple molecular substances causes this property.

23) Industrial diamonds are used in drill tips and precision cutting tools. What property of diamond makes it suitable for this use? Explain how the bonding in diamond causes its physical properties.

24) Describe and explain the differences between the physical properties of simple molecular substances and giant covalent substances.

* Answer on page 84

Balancing Equations

Equations crop up <u>everywhere</u> in chemistry — you can't hide from them. They show you just what's happening in a chemical reaction — what <u>reacts together</u> and what's <u>formed</u>.

Equations *Show the Reactants and Products of a Reaction*

A chemical reaction can be described as the process of going from REACTANTS to PRODUCTS.
You can write <u>word equations</u> or <u>symbol equations</u> to show any chemical reaction.

   e.g.   magnesium reacts with oxygen to produce magnesium oxide:

> Word equation: magnesium + oxygen $\rightarrow$ magnesium oxide
>
> Symbol equation: $2Mg$ + O_2 $\rightarrow$ $2MgO$
>
> (Mg) (Mg)   (O)(O)   (Mg)(O) (Mg)(O)

Look out for <u>state symbols</u> in equations — they tell you what <u>physical state</u> the reactants and products are in:

(s) — Solid	(l) — Liquid	(g) — Gas	(aq) — Aqueous (dissolved in water)

Here's the example with the state symbols in: $2Mg(s) + O_2(g) \rightarrow 2MgO(s)$

So, this is solid magnesium reacting with oxygen gas to make solid magnesium oxide.

Symbol Equations *Need to Be Balanced*

1) There must always be the <u>same</u> number of atoms on <u>both sides</u> — they can't just <u>disappear</u>.

2) You <u>balance</u> symbol equations by putting numbers <u>in front</u> of the formulae where needed.

Take this equation for burning propane in oxygen to make carbon dioxide and water:

$$C_3H_8 + O_2 \rightarrow CO_2 + H_2O$$

The <u>formulae</u> are all correct but the numbers of some atoms <u>don't match up</u> on both sides.
E.g. there are <u>three</u> carbon atoms on the left-hand side, but there's only <u>one</u> on the right-hand side.
You <u>can't change formulae</u>, like C_3H_8 to CH_8. You can only put numbers <u>in front of them</u>:

Method: *Balance just ONE type of atom at a time*

The more you practise, the quicker you'll get, but all you do is this:

> 1) Find an element that <u>doesn't balance</u> and <u>pencil in a number</u> to try and sort it out.
>
> 2) <u>See where it gets you</u>. It may create <u>another imbalance</u>, but pencil in <u>another number</u> and see where that gets you.
>
> 3) Carry on chasing <u>unbalanced</u> elements and it'll <u>sort itself out</u> pretty quickly.

<u>I'll show you</u>. In the equation above you soon notice we're short of H atoms on the RHS (right-hand side).

1) The only thing you can do about that is make it $4H_2O$ instead of just H_2O:

$$C_3H_8 + O_2 \rightarrow CO_2 + 4H_2O$$

2) We're also short of C atoms on the RHS, so to balance that up change CO_2 to $3CO_2$:

$$C_3H_8 + O_2 \rightarrow 3CO_2 + 4H_2O$$

3) Now the O atoms are out of balance. You can sort that out by making it $5O_2$ on the left-hand side:

$$C_3H_8 + 5O_2 \rightarrow 3CO_2 + 4H_2O$$

4) And suddenly there it is. <u>Everything balances</u>.

Balanced diet — a biscuit in one hand, an apple in the other...

Balance these symbol equations*: 1) $Fe_2O_3 + H_2 \rightarrow Fe + H_2O$ 2) $HCl + Al \rightarrow AlCl_3 + H_2$

Isotopes and Relative Atomic Mass

Some elements have more than one isotope. "But what's an isotope?" I hear you cry*. Read on...

Isotopes are the Same Except for an Extra Neutron or Two

A favourite exam question is: "Explain the meaning of the term isotope"
The trick is that it's impossible to explain what one isotope is. Nice of them that, isn't it!
You have to outsmart them and always start your answer "Isotopes are..." LEARN the definition:

> Isotopes are: different atomic forms of the same element, which have the SAME number of PROTONS but DIFFERENT numbers of NEUTRONS.

1) The upshot is: isotopes must have the same proton number but different mass numbers.
2) If they had different proton numbers, they'd be different elements altogether.
3) A very popular pair of isotopes are carbon-12 and carbon-14, used for carbon dating.

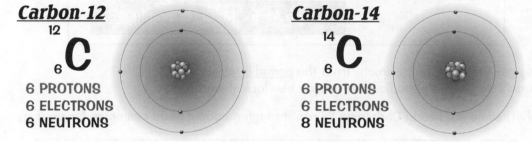

Carbon-12
$^{12}_{6}$C
6 PROTONS
6 ELECTRONS
6 NEUTRONS

Carbon-14
$^{14}_{6}$C
6 PROTONS
6 ELECTRONS
8 NEUTRONS

Relative Atomic Mass Takes All Stable Isotopes into Account

1) Relative atomic mass (A_r) is just a way of saying how heavy different atoms are compared with the mass of an atom of carbon-12. So carbon-12 has an A_r of exactly 12.
2) It's the average mass of all the isotopes of an element. It has to allow for the relative mass of each isotope and its relative abundance.
3) Relative abundance just means how much there is of each isotope compared to the total amount of the element in the world. This can be a ratio, a fraction or a percentage.

EXAMPLE: Work out the relative atomic mass of chlorine.

element	relative mass of isotope	relative abundance
chlorine	35	3
	37	1

This means that there are 2 isotopes of chlorine. One has a relative mass of 35 (^{35}Cl) and the other 37 (^{37}Cl).

The relative abundances show that there are 3 atoms of ^{35}Cl to every 1 of ^{37}Cl.

1) Multiply the mass of each isotope by its relative abundance.
2) Add those together.
3) Divide by the sum of the relative abundances.

$$A_r = \frac{(35 \times 3) + (37 \times 1)}{3 + 1} = \underline{35.5}$$

---

4) You can find the relative atomic mass of any element using the periodic table (see page 8).
5) Relative atomic masses don't usually come out as whole numbers or easy decimals, but they're often rounded to the nearest 0.5 in periodic tables.

Will this be in your exam? — isotope so...

Remember, isotopes have the same proton number but different mass numbers — you're gonna need to learn it.

---

*Not literally, of course. Just humour me, OK?   *Section 1 — Principles of Chemistry*

Relative Formula Mass

The biggest trouble with <u>relative formula mass</u> is that it <u>sounds</u> so blood-curdling.
It's very important though, so take a few deep breaths, and just enjoy, as the mists slowly clear...

Relative Formula Mass, M_r

If you have a compound like $MgCl_2$ then it has a <u>relative formula mass</u>, M_r, which is just all the relative atomic masses (see page 17) of the atoms it contains <u>added together</u>.

For $MgCl_2$ it would be:

$$MgCl_2$$

$$24 + (35.5 \times 2) = 95$$

So the M_r for $MgCl_2$ is simply <u>95</u>.

You can easily get the A_r for any element from the <u>periodic table</u>.
In the exam you'll be given a periodic table so you can look them up.

I'll tell you what, since it's nearly Christmas I'll run through a couple more examples for you:

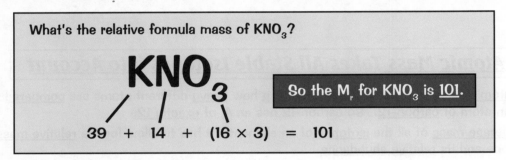

What's the relative formula mass of KNO_3?

$$KNO_3$$

So the M_r for KNO_3 is <u>101</u>.

$$39 + 14 + (16 \times 3) = 101$$

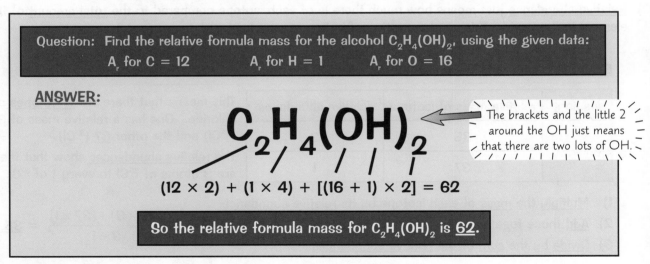

Question: Find the relative formula mass for the alcohol $C_2H_4(OH)_2$, using the given data:
A_r for C = 12 A_r for H = 1 A_r for O = 16

<u>ANSWER:</u>

$$C_2H_4(OH)_2$$

The brackets and the little 2 around the OH just means that there are two lots of OH.

$$(12 \times 2) + (1 \times 4) + [(16 + 1) \times 2] = 62$$

So the relative formula mass for $C_2H_4(OH)_2$ is <u>62</u>.

And that's all it is. A big fancy name like <u>relative formula mass</u> and all it means is "<u>add up all the mass numbers</u>". What a swizz, eh? You'd have thought it'd be something a bit juicier than that, wouldn't you. Still, that's life — it's all a big disappointment in the end. Sigh.

Numbers? — and you thought you were doing chemistry...

Make sure you learn the definition of relative formula mass — then have a go at this:
Find the relative formula mass of these compounds*: $NaOH$, Fe_2O_3, C_6H_{14}, $Mg(NO_3)_2$

Empirical and Molecular Formulae

This sounds a lot worse than it really is. Just follow the same method every time and you'll be laughing.

Finding the Empirical Formula (from Masses or Percentages)

1) The empirical formula gives you the smallest whole number ratio of atoms in a compound.
2) Try this for an easy peasy stepwise method for calculating an empirical formula:

> 1) List all the elements in the compound (there are usually only two or three).
> 2) Underneath them, write their experimental masses or percentages.
> 3) Divide each mass or percentage by the relative atomic mass (A_r) for that particular element.
> 4) Turn the numbers you get into a nice simple ratio by multiplying and/or dividing them by well-chosen numbers.
> 5) Get the ratio in its simplest form — that tells you the empirical formula of the compound.

Example: In an experiment, some iron oxide powder is reduced to pure metallic iron.
Use the following experimental data to find the empirical formula of the iron oxide used.

Mass of empty container	32.0 g
Mass of container + mass of iron oxide	96.0 g
Mass of container + iron	76.8 g

(A_r for iron = 56, A_r for oxygen = 16)

Method:
During the experiment oxygen is lost. The mass of oxygen lost is the difference between the mass of the container and iron oxide and the mass of the container and iron: 96.0 g − 76.8 g = 19.2 g.

The mass of iron made is the difference between the mass of the container with the iron and the mass of the empty container: 76.8 g − 32.0 g = 44.8 g.

1) List the two elements: Fe   O
2) Write in the experimental masses: 44.8   19.2
3) Divide by the A_r for each element: 44.8 ÷ 56 = 0.8   19.2 ÷ 16 = 1.2
4) Multiply by 10...   8   12
5) ...then divide by 4:   2   3

So the simplest formula is 2 atoms of Fe to 3 atoms of O, i.e. Fe_2O_3. And that's it done.

The Empirical Formula isn't Always the Same as the Molecular Formula

> The EMPIRICAL FORMULA of a compound is the simplest formula that tells you the ratio of different elements in the compound.
> The MOLECULAR FORMULA of a compound tells you the actual number of atoms of each element in a single molecule.

Molecular formulae are whole-number multiples of empirical formulae.

Example: A molecule has an empirical formula of $C_4H_3O_2$, and a relative molecular mass of 166.
Work out its molecular formula.

Method: 1) Find the mass of the empirical formula: (4 × 12) + (3 × 1) + (2 × 16) = 48 + 3 + 32 = 83 g
2) The relative molecular mass is 166, so there are 166 ÷ 83 = 2 empirical units in the molecule.
3) The molecular formula must be the empirical formula × 2, so the molecular formula must be $C_4H_3O_2$ × 2 = $C_8H_6O_4$. So there you go.

With this empirical formula I can rule the world — mwa ha ha ha...

Make sure you learn the five steps in the top purple box. Then try this example:
Find the empirical formula of the compound formed when 2.4 g of carbon reacts with 0.8 g of hydrogen.

Calculating Masses in Reactions

These can be kinda scary too, but chill out, little trembling one — just relax and enjoy.

The Three Important Steps — Not to be Missed...

1) Write out the balanced equation.

2) For the two bits you want, work out relative formula mass (M_r) and multiply them by the balancing numbers in the equation.

3) Apply the rule: Divide to get one, then multiply to get all. (But you have to apply this first to the substance they give information about, and then the other one!)

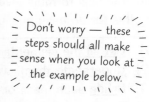
Don't worry — these steps should all make sense when you look at the example below.

Example   What mass of magnesium oxide is produced when 60 g of magnesium is burnt in air?

1) Write out the balanced equation: $2Mg + O_2 \rightarrow 2MgO$

2) Work out the relative formula masses of the two bits you want and multiply them by the balancing numbers in the equation:
   2Mg: $2 \times 24 = 48$ 2MgO: $2 \times (24 + 16) = 80$

Don't find the M_r of the oxygen here — you don't need it.

3) Apply the rule: Divide to get one, then multiply to get all.
   The two numbers, 48 and 80, tell us that 48 g of Mg react to give 80 g of MgO.
   Here's the tricky bit. We need to find out what happens when 60 g of Mg is burnt in air.

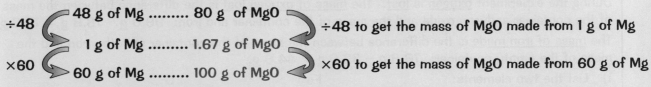

$\div48$ 48 g of Mg .... 80 g of MgO $\div48$ to get the mass of MgO made from 1 g of Mg
          1 g of Mg .... 1.67 g of MgO
$\times60$ 60 g of Mg .... 100 g of MgO $\times60$ to get the mass of MgO made from 60 g of Mg

This tells us that 60 g of magnesium will produce 100 g of magnesium oxide. If the question had said, "Find how much magnesium gives 500 g of magnesium oxide", you'd fill in the MgO side first, because that's the one you'd have the information about. Got it? Good-O!

The mass of product (in this case magnesium oxide) is called the yield of a reaction. Masses you calculate in this way are called theoretical yields. In practice you never get 100% of the yield, so the amount of product you get will be less than you calculated.

Percentage Yield Compares Actual and Theoretical Yield

The more reactant you start with, the higher the yield will be — that's pretty obvious. But the percentage yield doesn't depend on the amount of reactants you started with — it's a percentage.

1) The theoretical yield of a reaction can be calculated from the balanced equation (see above).

2) Percentage yield is given by the formula:

$$\text{percentage yield} = \frac{\text{actual yield (grams)}}{\text{theoretical yield (grams)}} \times 100$$

3) Percentage yield is always somewhere between 0 and 100%.

4) A 100% yield means that you got all the product you expected to get.

5) A 0% yield means that no reactants were converted into product, i.e. no product at all was made.

Paper 2

Reaction mass calculations — no worries, matey...

The only way to get good at these is to practise. So make sure you can do the example, then try these*:

1) Find the mass of calcium which gives 30 g of calcium oxide (CaO) when burnt in air.

2) What mass of fluorine (F_2) fully reacts with potassium to make 116 g of potassium fluoride (KF)?

Section 1 — Principles of Chemistry   *Answers on page 84.

Moles

The mole is really confusing. I think it's the word that puts people off. It's very difficult to see the relevance of the word "mole" to anything but a small burrowing animal.

"The Mole" is Simply the Name Given to a Certain Number

1) Just like "a million" is this many: 1 000 000; or "a billion" is this many: 1 000 000 000, so "a mole" is this many: 602 300 000 000 000 000 000 000 or 6.023×10^{23}.

2) And that's all it is. Just a number. The burning question, of course, is why is it such a silly long one like that, and with a six at the front?

3) The answer is that when you get precisely that number of atoms or molecules, of any element or compound, then, conveniently, they weigh exactly the same number of grams as the relative atomic mass, A_r (or relative formula mass, M_r) of the element or compound. This is arranged on purpose, of course, to make things easier.

4) One mole of atoms or molecules of any substance will have a mass in grams equal to the relative formula mass (A_r or M_r) for that substance.

EXAMPLES

Carbon has an A_r of 12.	So one mole of carbon weighs exactly 12 g.
Nitrogen gas, N_2, has an M_r of 28 (2 × 14).	So one mole of N_2 weighs exactly 28 g.
Carbon dioxide, CO_2, has an M_r of 44.	So one mole of CO_2 weighs exactly 44 g.

5) This means that 12 g of carbon, or 28 g of N_2, or 44 g of CO_2, all contain the same number of particles, namely one mole or 6.023×10^{23} atoms or molecules.

6) The molar mass of a substance is just another way of saying 'the mass of one mole'. Molar mass is measured in grams too. E.g. the molar mass of carbon is 12 g.

> **Paper 2** The number 6.023×10^{23} is called Avogadro's number or the Avogadro constant. So you can think of a mole as the Avogadro number of particles in a substance, where the particles are atoms, molecules, ions or electrons. **Paper 2**

Nice Easy Formula for Finding the Number of Moles in a Given Mass:

$$\text{Number of Moles} = \frac{\text{Mass in g} \quad \text{(of element or compound)}}{M_r \quad \text{(of element or compound)}}$$

Example: How many moles are there in 66 g of carbon dioxide?

Method: M_r of CO_2 = 12 + (16 × 2) = 44
No. of moles = Mass (g) ÷ M_r = 66 ÷ 44 = 1.5 moles. Easy Peasy.

7 moles of moles ≈ 1 Earth...

...assuming vol. of 1 mole = ¼ litre, no gaps between moles, spherical Earth...

Moles can definitely be a bit confusing. You need to be able to convert between moles and grams for the exam though — so spend a bit of time getting your head round all this if you need to.

Water of Crystallisation

Some salts are <u>hydrated</u> — their lattices contain <u>water molecules</u> as well as positive and negative ions.

Salts Can be Anhydrous or Hydrated

1) All solid salts consist of a <u>lattice</u> of positive and negative <u>ions</u> (see page 11).
2) In some salts, <u>water molecules</u> are incorporated in the lattice too.
3) The water in a lattice is called <u>water of crystallisation</u>.
4) A solid salt containing water of crystallisation is <u>hydrated</u>.
5) If a salt <u>doesn't</u> contain any water of crystallisation, it's called <u>anhydrous</u>.

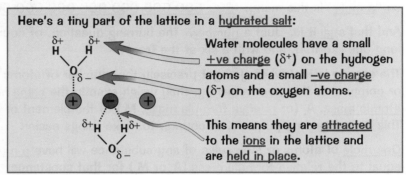

Here's a tiny part of the lattice in a <u>hydrated salt</u>:

Water molecules have a small <u>+ve charge</u> (δ^+) on the hydrogen atoms and a small <u>−ve charge</u> (δ^-) on the oxygen atoms.

This means they are <u>attracted</u> to the <u>ions</u> in the lattice and are <u>held in place</u>.

You Can Calculate How Much Water of Crystallisation a Salt Contains

1) One mole of a <u>hydrated salt</u> always has a <u>particular number of moles</u> of <u>water of crystallisation</u> — its <u>formula</u> shows <u>how many</u> (it's always a whole number).
2) For example, hydrated copper sulfate has <u>five moles of water</u> for every <u>one mole</u> of the salt. So its formula is $CuSO_4.5H_2O$. (Notice that there's a <u>dot</u> between the $CuSO_4$ and the $5H_2O$.)
3) Many hydrated salts <u>lose</u> their water of crystallisation when <u>heated</u>, to become <u>anhydrous</u>. If you know the mass of the salt when it's hydrated <u>and</u> when it's anhydrous, you can work its <u>formula</u> out like this:

Example: Heating hydrated magnesium sulfate, $MgSO_4.XH_2O$, in a crucible forms <u>anhydrous</u> magnesium sulfate, $MgSO_4$. Use the experimental data below to find the <u>value of X</u> and write the <u>formula</u> of the <u>hydrated salt</u>.

Mass of empty crucible	42.000 g
Mass of crucible + $MgSO_4.XH_2O$	45.210 g
Mass of crucible + $MgSO_4$	43.567 g

Method:
1) First, work out what <u>mass</u> of $MgSO_4.XH_2O$ and $MgSO_4$ you have.
   Mass of $MgSO_4.XH_2O$ = 45.210 − 42.000 = 3.210 g
   Mass of $MgSO_4$ = 43.567 − 42.000 = 1.567 g
2) Calculate the <u>number of moles</u> of <u>water lost</u>.
   Mass of water lost: 3.210 − 1.567 = 1.643 g
   Number of moles of water lost: mass ÷ M_r = 1.643 g ÷ 18 = 0.0913 moles

   $M_r H_2O = (2 \times 1) + 16 = 18$
3) Calculate the <u>number of moles</u> of <u>anhydrous salt</u> made.
   Molar mass of $MgSO_4$: 24 + 32 + (4 × 16) = 120 g/mol
   Number of moles $MgSO_4$: mass ÷ M_r = 1.567 ÷ 120 = 0.0131 moles
4) Work out the <u>ratio of moles</u> of <u>anhydrous salt</u> to <u>moles of water</u>.
   From the experiment, 0.0131 moles of salt : 0.0913 moles of water,
   So, 1 mole of salt : (0.0913 ÷ 0.0131) = 6.97 moles of water
5) X must be a <u>whole number</u>, and some errors are to be expected in any experiment, so you can <u>round off</u> your result — X = 7 and the formula of the hydrated salt is $MgSO_4.7H_2O$.

Nine-headed water bear — Hydra-ted...

This working-out-the-formula business can be a bit tricky to get your head around at first — but if you follow exactly the <u>same method</u> each time you'll soon work it out. Oh, and don't forget the dot . it's very important.

Calculating Volumes

Run for your lives now, while you've still got the chance — it's equations and stuff.

Avogadro's Law — One Mole of Any Gas Occupies 24 dm³

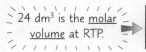

dm³ is a fancy way of writing 'litre', so 1 dm³ = 1000 cm³

The space that one mole of a gas takes up is called its molar volume.
Here's a handy fact about molar volume that you definitely need to learn:

24 dm³ is the molar volume at RTP.

> One mole of any gas always occupies 24 dm³ (= 24 000 cm³) at room temperature and pressure (RTP: 25 °C and 1 atmosphere)

This means you can use the formulae below to convert the number of moles, or mass, of any gas to a volume:

$$\text{VOLUME (dm}^3\text{)} = \text{moles of gas} \times 24$$

$$\text{VOLUME (dm}^3\text{)} = \frac{\text{mass of gas}}{M_r \text{ of gas}} \times 24$$

EXAMPLE 1 What's the volume of 4.5 moles of chlorine at RTP?

Answer: volume of 1 mole = 24 dm³, so volume of 4.5 moles = 4.5 × 24 dm³ = 108 dm³

EXAMPLE 2 How many moles are there in 8280 cm³ of hydrogen gas at RTP?

Answer: Number of moles = $\dfrac{\text{Volume of gas}}{\text{Volume of 1 mole}} = \dfrac{8.28}{24} = 0.345 \text{ moles}$

Don't forget to convert from cm³ to dm³.

You Can Calculate Volumes in Reactions If You Know the Masses

For this type of question there are two stages:
1) Find the reacting mass, exactly like in the examples on page 20.
2) Then convert the mass into a volume using the formula above.

> Example: Find the volume of carbon dioxide produced (at room T and P) when 2.7 g of carbon is completely burned in oxygen. (A_r of carbon = 12, A_r of oxygen = 16)
>
> Method:
> 1) Balanced equation: $C + O_2 \rightarrow CO_2$
> 2) Write down the M_r for each: ÷12   12   32   44   ÷12
> 3) Divide for one, times for all: 1 .... 3.666...
>   ×2.7   2.7 .... 9.9   ×2.7
>
> 4) So 2.7 g of C gives 9.9 g of CO₂.
>   Now the new bit:
>   Using the above formula: $\text{Volume} = \dfrac{\text{MASS}}{M_r} \times 24$
>
> so Volume = (MASS/M_r) × 24 = (9.9/44) × 24 = 5.4 dm³

That's ANY gas — oxygen, methane, carbon dioxide, ANY gas...

All this stuff ties in with page 20 — if you're not comfortable working out the reacting masses have a look there first. The only new thing here is the molar volume business: 1 mole of gas = 24 000 cm³. Easy.

Moles and Concentration

Concentration is all about "how much" stuff you have in a solution.

Concentration _is the_ 'Amount of Stuff' _per_ Unit Volume

1) The concentration of a solution is usually measured in moles per dm^3 (i.e. moles per litre). So 1 mole of stuff in 1 dm^3 of solution has a concentration of 1 mole per dm^3 (or 1 mol/dm^3).

2) You might also sometimes see concentration being measured in grams per dm^3. So 56 grams of stuff dissolved in 1 dm^3 of solution has a concentration of 56 g per dm^3 (or 56 g/dm^3).

Concentration = No. of Moles ÷ Volume

1) If you ever have to find the concentration of a solution, here's the formula triangle you'll need:

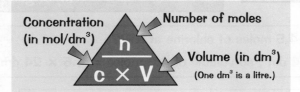

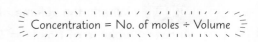

Concentration = No. of moles ÷ Volume

Example 1: What's the concentration of a solution with 2 moles of potassium iodide in 500 cm^3?

Answer: Easy — you've got 2 moles of potassium iodide and 500 cm^3 = 0.5 dm^3.
So just stick these numbers in the formula: Concentration = 2 ÷ 0.5 = 4 mol/dm^3

2) You can use the same formula triangle to find the number of moles that are in a solution:

Example 2: How many moles of sodium chloride are in 250 cm^3 of a 3 mol/dm^3 solution?

Answer: 250 cm^3 = 0.25 dm^3. So, using the formula from the triangle...
Number of moles = concentration × volume = 3 × 0.25 = 0.75 moles

Converting _Moles per dm^3_ to _Grams per dm^3_

1) Calculating concentrations in grams per dm^3 is easy. You just divide the mass of the chemical in grams by the volume of solvent you used to dissolve it in dm^3.

Example 1: Give the concentration in g/dm^3 of a solution made by dissolving 3 g of NaCl in 100 cm^3 of water.

Answer: Concentration = mass (g) ÷ volume (dm^3) = 3 ÷ 0.1 = 30 g/dm^3

2) Changing a concentration from mol/dm^3 to g/dm^3 isn't too tricky. All you need to do is use the formula you met on page 21 to convert the moles per dm^3 into mass per dm^3.

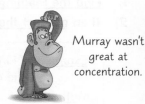

Murray wasn't great at concentration.

Example 2: You have a 0.04 mol/dm^3 solution of sulfuric acid. What is the concentration in grams per dm^3?

Step 1: Work out the relative formula mass of the chemical.
So, H_2SO_4 = (1 × 2) + 32 + (16 × 4) = 98

Step 2: Convert the concentration in moles into concentration in grams.
So, in 1 dm^3: Mass in grams = moles × relative formula mass = 0.04 × 98 = 3.92 g
So the concentration in g/dm^3 = 3.92 g/dm^3

Learning this may take some concentration...

The main thing to learn on this page is the formula triangle for calculating concentration — remember that and concentration calculations should be a breeze. It'll come in handy when you do titrations too (see page 53).

Electrical Conductivity

Electrical conductivity is all about the <u>movement</u> of electrons or ions.

Electric Current *is a Flow of* Electrons *or* Ions

1) <u>Electrons</u> have a <u>negative</u> charge. <u>Ions</u> can have either a <u>negative</u> or a <u>positive</u> charge.
2) When electrons or ions <u>move</u>, they can cause the material they're in to <u>conduct electricity</u>.
3) The electric current is the <u>flow</u> of the electrons or ions.

Ionic Compounds *Only* Conduct Electricity *when Molten or in Solution*

1) Ionic compounds are made of a <u>lattice</u> of <u>positive and negative ions</u> (more on this on pages 10-11).
2) <u>Solid</u> ionic compounds <u>don't</u> conduct electricity because the ions <u>aren't</u> able to move around.
3) When an ionic compound is <u>dissolved</u> the ions separate and are <u>able to move</u> in the <u>solution</u>. This means that the compound will <u>conduct electricity</u>.
4) When an ionic compound <u>melts</u>, the ions are also <u>able to move</u> so the compound can <u>conduct electricity</u>.

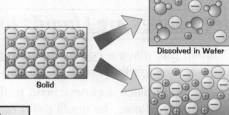

Solid

Dissolved in Water

Melted

Covalent Compounds Don't *Conduct Electricity*

1) Covalent compounds <u>don't contain ions</u> because they make bonds by sharing electrons (see page 12).
2) This means that they don't have any charged particles that are able to <u>move</u> — so they <u>can't</u> conduct electricity.

An important exception to this rule is graphite (page 14). Graphite has delocalised electrons so it's a good electrical conductor.

Metals *are Held Together by Metallic Bonding*

1) Metals have a <u>giant structure</u> of <u>positive ions</u> surrounded by a <u>sea of delocalised electrons</u>.
2) The <u>attraction</u> between the positive ions and the electrons is called <u>metallic bonding</u>.
3) It's this metallic bonding which gives metals their <u>properties</u>.

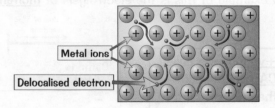

Metal ions

Delocalised electron

Metals *are* Good Conductors *of* Electricity *and* Heat

The <u>delocalised electrons</u> are able to <u>move</u> through the structure. This means metals can conduct <u>electricity</u>. The movement of electrons also means <u>energy</u> can be transferred quickly through the material, so metals are good conductors of <u>heat</u>.

Don't try this at home. You'll die.

Most Metals are Malleable

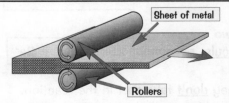

Sheet of metal

Rollers

The layers of atoms in a metal can <u>slide</u> over each other, making metals malleable — this means that they can be <u>hammered</u> or <u>rolled</u> into <u>flat sheets</u>.

Why do ions hate electrons? — they're so negative...

This page isn't so bad... you've just got to remember what an <u>electrical current</u> is and how the <u>structure</u> and <u>bonding</u> of <u>metals</u>, <u>ionic compounds</u> and <u>covalent compounds</u> can explain their <u>properties</u>. Enjoy.

Electrolysis

Well, you are in for a treat. The last three pages of this section are all about <u>electrolysis</u>. Oooooooooh...

Electrolysis *is Used to Make New Substances*

1) If you pass an <u>electric current</u> through an <u>ionic substance</u> that's <u>molten</u> or <u>in solution</u> it breaks down into <u>new substances</u>. This is called <u>electrolysis</u>.

2) It requires a <u>liquid</u> to <u>conduct</u> the <u>electricity</u>, called the <u>electrolyte</u>.

3) Electrolytes are made by <u>melting</u> or <u>dissolving ionic compounds</u>.

4) In either case it's the <u>free ions</u> which <u>conduct</u> the electricity.

5) For the circuit to be complete, there's got to be a <u>flow of electrons</u>. <u>Electrons</u> are taken <u>away from</u> ions at a <u>positive electrode (anode)</u> and <u>given to</u> other ions at a <u>negative electrode (cathode)</u>.

6) As ions gain or lose electrons they become <u>atoms</u> or <u>molecules</u>.

There's a diagram showing how electrolysis works at the bottom of the page.

Electrolytes *are Liquids that Conduct Electricity*

1) When you place a <u>conductivity probe</u> in an <u>electrolyte</u>, <u>current</u> flows through the circuit — so you can <u>measure</u> its <u>conductivity</u>.

2) When you place a conductivity probe in a <u>non-electrolyte</u>, <u>no current</u> flows, so you'll get a reading of <u>zero</u> conductivity.

3) Another way of determining whether a substance is an electrolyte or not is to set up an <u>electrolytic cell</u> (like the one below).

4) If the substance will <u>undergo electrolysis</u> then it <u>is</u> an electrolyte.

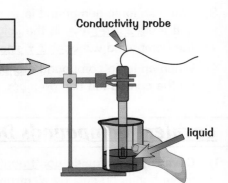

Conductivity probe

liquid

In Molten *Ionic Compounds There's Only One Source of Ions*

1) <u>Molten</u> ionic compounds can be electrolysed because the ions can <u>move freely</u>.

2) They're usually broken up into their <u>elements</u>.

3) A good example of this is the electrolysis of <u>molten lead bromide</u> ($PbBr_2$):

You can melt lead bromide using a Bunsen burner.

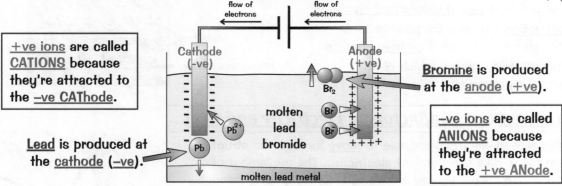

+ve ions are called CATIONS because they're attracted to the −ve CAThode.

Bromine is produced at the <u>anode (+ve)</u>.

−ve ions are called ANIONS because they're attracted to the +ve ANode.

Lead is produced at the <u>cathode (−ve)</u>.

4) You can write <u>half-equations</u> to show what's happening at each <u>electrode</u>.

5) The +ve Pb^{2+} ions are attracted to the −ve cathode. At the <u>cathode</u> a lead ion <u>accepts two electrons</u> to become a <u>lead atom</u>. The <u>molten lead</u> that forms will <u>sink</u> to the bottom.

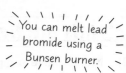 $Pb^{2+} + 2e^- \rightarrow Pb$

6) The −ve Br^- ions are attracted to the +ve anode. At the <u>anode</u> two bromide ions <u>lose one electron</u> each and become a <u>bromine molecule</u>. Brown <u>bromine gas</u> forms at the <u>top</u> of the anode.

$2Br^- \rightarrow Br_2 + 2e^-$

7) The <u>electrodes</u> are made from an <u>inert</u> (unreactive) material so they <u>don't</u> take part in the reaction.

Faster shopping at the supermarket — use electrolleys...

<u>Electrolysis</u> is brilliant for removing unwanted hair from your body. Good for women with moustaches, or men with hairy backs. And good for beauty clinics too — makes them some cash. Oh, wait, that's a different kind of electrolysis...

Electrolysis

Here's another lovely page all about electrolysis. Enjoy.

Electrolysis of Aqueous Solutions is a Bit More Complicated

1) In aqueous solutions, as well as the ions from the ionic compound, there will be hydrogen ions (H^+) and hydroxide ions (OH^-) from the water.

2) At the cathode, if H^+ ions and metal ions are present, hydrogen gas will be produced if the metal ions are more reactive than the H^+ ions (e.g. sodium ions). If the metal ions are less reactive than the H^+ ions (e.g. copper ions), a solid layer of the pure metal will be produced instead.

3) At the anode, if OH^- and halide ions (Cl^-, Br^-, I^-) are present, molecules of chlorine, bromine or iodine will be formed. If no halide ions are present, then oxygen will be formed.

4) Here are three examples that you need to know about:

Sulfuric Acid:

A solution of sulfuric acid (H_2SO_4) contains three different ions: SO_4^{2-}, H^+ and OH^-.

- Hydrogen ions (from the water or sulfuric acid) accept electrons. So at the cathode, hydrogen gas is produced.

$$2H^+ + 2e^- \rightarrow H_2$$

- Hydroxide ions lose electrons more easily than sulfate ions. So at the anode oxygen and water are produced.

$$4OH^- \rightarrow O_2 + 2H_2O + 4e^-$$

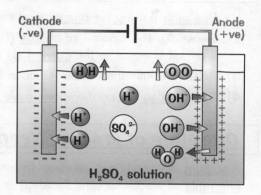

Sodium Chloride:

A solution of sodium chloride (NaCl) contains four different ions: Na^+, Cl^-, OH^- and H^+.

- Hydrogen ions accept electrons more easily than sodium ions. So at the cathode, hydrogen gas is produced.

$$2H^+ + 2e^- \rightarrow H_2$$

- Chloride ions lose electrons more easily than hydroxide ions. So at the anode chlorine gas is produced.

$$2Cl^- \rightarrow Cl_2 + 2e^-$$

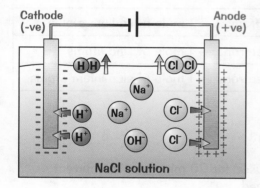

Copper(II) Sulfate:

A solution of copper(II) sulfate ($CuSO_4$) contains four different ions: Cu^{2+}, SO_4^{2-}, H^+ and OH^-.

- Copper ions accept electrons more easily than hydrogen ions. So at the cathode, copper metal is produced.

$$Cu^{2+} + 2e^- \rightarrow Cu$$

- Hydroxide ions lose electrons more easily than sulfate ions. So at the anode oxygen and water are produced.

$$4OH^- \rightarrow O_2 + 2H_2O + 4e^-$$

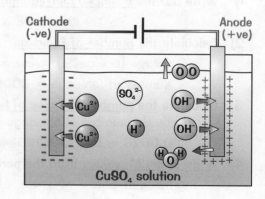

If only revision was made up of positive ions...

Then we could reduce it using electrolysis. This page is a bit tricky. You need to make sure that you can remember the half-equations for all three electrolytes at both electrodes... Phew. I think I need to lie down.

Electrolysis — Calculating Masses

Will the electrolysis never end... (Well, yes — this is the end of the section, huzzah.)

No. of Electrons Transferred Increases with Time and Current

1) The amount of product made by electrolysis depends on the number of electrons that are transferred.

2) If you increase the number of electrons, you increase the amount of substance produced.

This can be achieved by:
- electrolysing for a longer time.
- increasing the current.

Coulombs and Faradays are Amounts of Electricity

1) One amp flowing for one second means a charge of one coulomb has moved.

2) Generally, the amount of charge (Q, measured in coulombs) flowing through a circuit is equal to the current (I) measured in amps multiplied by the time in seconds (t):

$$Q = I\,t$$

3) 96 000 coulombs (amps × seconds) is called one faraday.

4) One faraday (F) contains one mole of electrons.

One Mole of Product Needs 'n' Moles of Electrons

A sodium ion needs one electron to make a sodium atom. So one mole of sodium ions is going to need one mole of electrons (one faraday) to make one mole of sodium atoms. But an ion with a 2^+ charge needs two moles of electrons to make one mole of atoms, and, guess what, three for a 3^+ charge...

$Na^+ + e^- \rightarrow Na$	1 mole of sodium ions + 1 mole of electrons → 1 mole of sodium atoms
$Zn^{2+} + 2e^- \rightarrow Zn$	1 mole of zinc ions + 2 moles of electrons → 1 mole of zinc atoms
$Al^{3+} + 3e^- \rightarrow Al$	1 mole of aluminium ions + 3 moles of electrons → 1 mole of aluminium atoms

Use These Steps in Calculations

EXAMPLE: Some molten lead(II) chloride ($PbCl_2$) is electrolysed for 20 minutes. The current flowing is 5 amps. Find the mass of lead produced.

1) Write out the balanced half-equation for the cathode.

$$Pb^{2+} + 2e^- \rightarrow Pb$$

Writing the half-equation is easier if you remember that the full equation is: $PbCl_2 \rightarrow Pb + Cl_2$

2) Calculate the number of faradays.

Charge (coulombs) = current (amps) × time (s) = 5 × (20 × 60) = 6000 coulombs.

Number of faradays = 6000 / 96 000 = 0.0625 F

3) Calculate the number of moles of lead produced.

(divide the number of faradays by the number of electrons in the half-equation)

0.0625 ÷ 2 = 0.03125 moles of lead atoms.

4) Write in the M_r values from the periodic table to work out the mass of solid lead produced.

Mass of lead = M_r × No. of moles = 207 × 0.03125 = 6.5 g (to 1 d.p.)

The more time you spend on this page, the more you'll learn...

This stuff isn't easy. So take your time over it. Read it through once. If you don't get it, read it through again. If you still don't get it, have a cup of tea before reading it again. That should help.

Paper 2

Revision Summary for Section 1 — 2

Right. Here you go. One list of very important questions to test whether you've learnt this section properly. There's no backing out now — make sure you can answer each and every one of these questions, without any sneaky peeks. If you're struggling, go back through the section, have a browse and then try again. Repeat this until you can do them all perfectly. Have fun.

1) What do the following state symbols stand for?
   a) (l)   b) (aq)   c) (g)

2)* Balance these symbol equations:
   a) $Na + H_2O \rightarrow NaOH + H_2$ b) $Al + HCl \rightarrow AlCl_3 + H_2$

3) Define the term isotope.

4)* The table below gives the masses and relative abundances of the isotopes of neon:

relative mass of isotope	relative abundance
20	91%
22	9%

   Calculate the relative atomic mass of neon. Give your answer to 2 decimal places.

5)* Find the relative formula mass of the following compounds. (Hint: there's a Periodic table on p.8.)
   a) H_2SO_4 b) $ZnCO_3$ c) CH_3COONa d) $C(CH_3)_4$

6)* Using the periodic table, find the empirical formula of the compound formed when 227 g of calcium reacts with 216 g of fluorine.

7)* A molecule has an empirical formula of C_2H_5Cl, and a relative molecular mass of 258. Work out its molecular formula.

8)* a) What mass of sodium oxide (Na_2O) is produced when 50 g of sodium is burnt in air?
   b) Briony does this reaction and ends up with 42.3 g of sodium oxide. What is the percentage yield of her reaction?

9)* How many moles are there in 147 g of sodium hydroxide (NaOH)?

10)* What is the mass of 0.05 moles of magnesium oxide (MgO)?

11)* Heating hydrated iron chloride, $FeCl_2.XH_2O$, in a crucible forms anhydrous iron chloride, $FeCl_2$. Using the experimental data below, find the value of X and write the formula of the hydrated salt.

Mass of empty crucible	23.299 g
Mass of crucible + mass $FeCl_2.XH_2O$	28.133 g
Mass of crucible + $FeCl_2$	26.347 g

12)* What's the volume of 3.7 moles of nitrogen at RTP?

13)* How many moles of sodium hydroxide are in 250 cm³ of a 2 mol/dm³ solution of NaOH?

14)* 0.55 moles of sodium sulfate are dissolved in 500 cm³ of water. What is the concentration in mol/dm³ of the solution made?

15) When are ionic compounds able to conduct electricity?

16) Covalent compounds don't usually conduct electricity. Explain why.

17) Why are metals good conductors of heat and electricity?

18) Describe an experiment to determine whether a solution is an electrolyte or a non-electrolyte.

19) Draw and label a diagram to show the electrolysis of lead(II) bromide.

20) Write the half-equations for the electrolysis of copper(II) sulfate, $CuSO_4$.

21)* Find the mass of lead liberated if 3 amps flows for 40 minutes during the electrolysis of lead(II) bromide ($PbBr_2$).

* Answers on page 84.

More About the Periodic Table

Remember that big ol' periodic table back on page 8. Well there's more about it on this page here.
It has all the elements in a nice logical order, which makes it great for spotting trends. Honest.

The Periodic Table is Arranged in Periods and Groups

Periods

1) The rows are called periods.
2) The properties of elements change as you go along a period (sometimes quite dramatically).

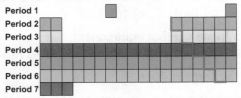

You can find the full periodic table with all the elements shown on page 8.

Groups

1) The columns of the periodic table are called groups.
2) Elements in the same group have similar chemical properties. This is because they have the same number of electrons in their outer shell (learn this).
3) The properties of elements (such as reactivity) often gradually change as you go down a group (i.e. as the atomic number increases).

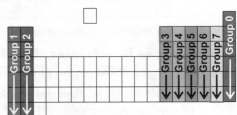

The Elements can be Classified as Metals or Non-Metals

The periodic table can be split into two parts — the metals are on one side and the non-metals are on the other.

Metals

1) The elements on the left of the zigzag are all classified as metals.
2) Metals conduct electricity because they allow charge to pass through them easily.
3) Metal oxides are basic. This means they will neutralise acids. Metal oxides which dissolve will form solutions with a pH of more than 7.

Non-metals

1) The elements on the right of the zigzag are all classified as non-metals.
2) Non-metals are poor conductors of electricity.
3) Non-metal oxides are acidic. They dissolve in water to form solutions with a pH of less than 7.

Group 0 Elements are All Inert, Colourless Gases

1) Group 0 elements are called the noble gases and include the elements helium, neon and argon (plus a few others).
2) They are inert — this means they don't react with much at all.
3) The reason for this is that they have a full outer shell of electrons. This means they're not desperate to give up or gain electrons.

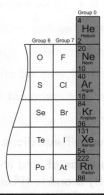

They don't react — that's Noble De use to us chemists...

Well, they don't react so there's not much to learn about the noble gases — and a question about them is likely to be easy marks in the exam. Don't forget the other stuff here — make sure you learn everything on this page.

Group 1 — The Alkali Metals

Alkali metals all have <u>one electron</u> in their outermost shell, which makes them very <u>reactive</u>. <u>Lithium</u>, <u>sodium</u> and <u>potassium</u> are the stars of the show here...

Group 1 Elements All React in a Similar Way with Water

1) <u>Simple reactions</u> can be used to work out if an element is part of the same <u>family</u> as other elements. Elements of the same family will react in a similar way.

2) For example, when <u>lithium</u>, <u>sodium</u> and <u>potassium</u> are put in <u>water</u>, they all react <u>vigorously</u>.

3) The <u>reaction</u> produces a <u>metal hydroxide</u> solution. This solution is <u>alkaline</u> — this is why Group 1 elements are known as the <u>alkali metals</u>.

4) The <u>reaction</u> of the alkali metals with water also produces <u>hydrogen</u> — this is why you can see <u>fizzing</u>.

5) These reactions can be written as <u>chemical equations</u> — e.g. for <u>sodium</u> the equation is...

Word equation: sodium + water → sodium hydroxide + hydrogen

Symbol equation: $2Na_{(s)} + 2H_2O_{(l)} \rightarrow 2NaOH_{(aq)} + H_{2(g)}$

<u>STATE SYMBOLS</u>: (s) = <u>solid</u>, (l) = <u>liquid</u>, (aq) = <u>aqueous</u> (dissolved in water), (g) = <u>gas</u>

Group 1 Elements Become More Reactive Down the Group

1) As you go <u>down</u> Group 1 the elements become <u>more reactive</u>.

2) You can see this in the <u>rate of reaction</u> with water (i.e. the time taken for a lump of the same size of each element to <u>react completely</u> with the water and disappear).

3) <u>Lithium</u> takes longer than sodium or potassium to react, so it's the <u>least reactive</u>.

4) <u>Potassium</u> takes the shortest time to react of these three elements, so it's the <u>most reactive</u>.

> The elements in <u>GROUP 1</u> get <u>MORE REACTIVE</u> as the <u>ATOMIC NUMBER INCREASES</u>.

REACTIONS WITH WATER

universal indicator | Lithium — The lump of lithium moves slowly around the surface, fizzing, until it disappears.

Water (neutral)

time of reaction 00:30

The water has become alkaline so the indicator solution turns purple.

Sodium — Sodium fizzes rapidly and moves quickly around the surface, and may ignite.

00:20

Potassium — Potassium reacts vigorously, burns with a lilac flame — and sometimes explodes.

00:05

Group 1	Group 2
7 Li Lithium 3	Be
23 Na Sodium 11	Mg
39 K Potassium 19	Ca
86 Rb Rubidium 37	Sr
133 Cs Caesium 55	Ba
223 Fr Francium 87	Ra

Atoms Lose Electrons More Easily Down the Group

1) All <u>Group 1</u> metals have <u>1 electron</u> in their outer shell.

2) As you go <u>down</u> Group 1, the <u>outermost electron</u> is in a shell that's <u>further from the nucleus</u>.

3) Which means the <u>attraction</u> between the <u>outermost electron</u> and the <u>nucleus</u> becomes <u>less</u>.

4) So as you go down Group 1 the atoms get <u>bigger</u>, the outer electron is <u>more easily lost</u>, and the metals are <u>more reactive</u>.

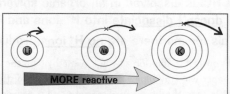

MORE reactive

Paper 2

My cat is from group 1 — it reacts vigorously with water...

Alkali metals are ace. They're <u>so reactive</u> you have to store them in <u>oil</u> — because otherwise they'd react with the air. AND they <u>fizz</u> in water and <u>burn</u> and <u>explode</u> and everything. <u>Cool</u>.

Group 7 — The Halogens

The halogens are all <u>one electron short</u> of having a full outer shell.

HALOGEN — Seven Letters — Group 7

1) The elements in <u>Group 7</u> of the periodic table are called the <u>halogens</u>.

2) The <u>properties</u> of the elements in <u>Group 7</u> change <u>gradually</u> as you go <u>down</u> the group (i.e. as the atomic number <u>increases</u>). Look at the table below.

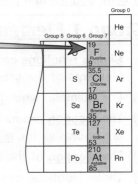

	Properties			
Group VII Elements	Atomic number	Colour	Physical state at room temperature	Boiling point
Chlorine	17	green	gas	−34 °C
Bromine	35	red-brown	liquid	59 °C
Iodine	53	dark grey	solid	185 °C

3) As the <u>atomic number</u> of the halogens <u>increases</u>, the elements have a <u>darker colour</u> and a <u>higher boiling point</u> (which is why they go from <u>gases</u> at the top of Group 7 to <u>solids</u> at the bottom, at room temperature).

4) The <u>higher up</u> Group 7 an element is, the <u>more reactive</u> it is. This is because the shell with the missing electron is <u>nearer to the nucleus</u>, so the pull from the <u>positive nucleus</u> is <u>greater</u>.

5) You might need to use these trends to <u>predict</u> the properties of <u>other halogens</u>, e.g. fluorine.

Hydrogen Chloride Gas <u>Dissociates in</u> <u>Water...</u>

1) Halogens can combine with hydrogen to form <u>hydrogen halides</u>, for example, <u>hydrogen chloride</u> and <u>hydrogen bromide</u>.

2) <u>Hydrogen chloride</u> has the chemical formula <u>HCl</u> and is a <u>gas</u> at room temperature.

3) When hydrogen chloride is dissolved in water the HCl molecules <u>split up</u> into H^+ ions and Cl^- ions — this process is called <u>dissociation</u>.

4) The solution that is formed is called <u>hydrochloric acid</u>.

5) Hydrochloric acid is an <u>acidic solution</u> (obviously) because it contains H^+ ions.

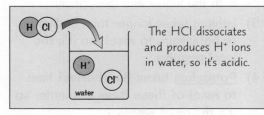

The HCl dissociates and produces H^+ ions in water, so it's acidic.

If you test a solution of hydrochloric acid with <u>blue litmus paper</u> the paper will turn <u>red/pink</u>.

...but Not in <u>Methylbenzene</u>

1) If HCl is dissolved in an organic solvent like <u>methylbenzene</u>, it <u>doesn't dissociate</u> into H^+ ions and Cl^- ions.

2) This means there are <u>no H^+ ions</u> produced so it's <u>not acidic</u>.

If you test a solution of HCl in methylbenzene with <u>blue litmus paper</u> the paper will <u>stay blue</u>. But if there is <u>any moisture</u> on the paper or in the bottle then the HCl <u>can dissociate</u> and it will behave like an <u>acid</u> again.

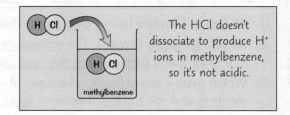

The HCl doesn't dissociate to produce H^+ ions in methylbenzene, so it's not acidic.

They're great, the halogens — you have to hand it to them...

Halogens are <u>really useful</u> and loads of <u>everyday things</u> contain them, e.g. <u>toothpaste</u> and the <u>non-stick coating</u> on frying pans. But on their own, they're <u>poisonous</u>. <u>Chlorine's</u> good because it <u>kills bacteria</u> — it's used in <u>bleach</u> and <u>swimming pools</u>. <u>Iodine</u> is used as an antiseptic, to prevent cuts from being <u>infected</u>.

Displacement Reactions

The halogens are a competitive lot. The **more reactive** ones will **push** the others out of a compound. How rude...

More Reactive Halogens will Displace Less Reactive Ones

1) The elements in Group 7 take part in <u>displacement reactions</u>.

2) A <u>displacement reaction</u> is where a <u>more reactive</u> element "pushes out" (displaces) a <u>less reactive</u> element from a compound.

3) For example, <u>chlorine</u> is more reactive than <u>iodine</u> (it's higher up Group 7).

4) So, if you add <u>chlorine water</u> to <u>potassium iodide</u> solution the chlorine will react with the potassium in the potassium iodide to form <u>potassium chloride</u>.

5) The <u>iodine</u> is <u>displaced from the salt</u> and gets left in the solution, turning it <u>brown</u>.

6) The table below shows what happens when you mix different combinations of <u>chlorine</u>, <u>bromine</u> and <u>iodine</u> with the salts <u>potassium chloride</u>, <u>potassium bromide</u> and <u>potassium iodide</u>.

	Potassium chloride solution KCl(aq) — colourless	Potassium bromide solution KBr(aq) — colourless	Potassium iodide solution KI(aq) — colourless
Chlorine water $Cl_{2(aq)}$ — colourless	no reaction	orange solution (Br_2) formed	brown solution (I_2) formed
Bromine water $Br_{2(aq)}$ — orange	no reaction	no reaction	brown solution (I_2) formed
Iodine water $I_{2(aq)}$ — brown	no reaction	no reaction	no reaction

These experiments are dead easy. All you need to do is add a <u>few drops</u> of the <u>halogen solution</u> to the <u>salt solution</u>. Then look for a <u>colour change</u>.

Halogen Displacement Reactions Involve Transfer of Electrons

1) You can show the <u>displacement reactions</u> between halogens and salt solutions as <u>equations</u>. E.g.

$$Cl_{2(aq)} + 2KI_{(aq)} \rightarrow I_{2(aq)} + 2KCl_{(aq)}$$

This is the equation for chlorine displacing iodine from potassium iodide. They might give you a different example in the exam, but the principle is always the same.

2) When this reaction happens <u>electrons</u> are <u>passed</u> from the iodine to the chlorine.

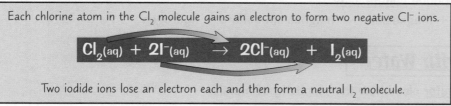

Each chlorine atom in the Cl_2 molecule gains an electron to form two negative Cl^- ions.

$$Cl_{2(aq)} + 2I^-_{(aq)} \rightarrow 2Cl^-_{(aq)} + I_{2(aq)}$$

Two iodide ions lose an electron each and then form a neutral I_2 molecule.

3) A <u>loss of electrons</u> is called <u>oxidation</u>. A <u>gain in electrons</u> is called <u>reduction</u>.

4) In displacement reactions, reduction and oxidation happen <u>simultaneously</u> — for example, in this reaction the <u>chlorine is reduced</u> and the <u>iodine is oxidised</u>.

You can remember which is which by using <u>OIL RIG</u>. <u>O</u>xidation <u>I</u>s <u>L</u>oss, <u>R</u>eduction <u>I</u>s <u>G</u>ain (of electrons).

5) An <u>oxidising agent</u> accepts electrons and <u>gets reduced</u>. So, here <u>chlorine</u> is an oxidising agent.

6) A <u>reducing agent</u> donates electrons and <u>gets oxidised</u>. So <u>iodine</u> is a reducing agent.

7) Reactions where reduction and oxidation happen at the same time are called <u>redox reactions</u>.

Redox — a nice relaxing bubble bath...

...or the most mind exploding concept ever. Redox reactions are definitely tricky to get your head around and the best way to get through it is to remember OIL RIG — <u>Oxidation Is Loss, Reduction Is Gain</u> (of electrons). This handy little memory aid will definitely help you out with all types of tricky redox questions. Promise.

Reactions of Metals

You can use the reactions of different metals with <u>dilute acids</u> to work out how <u>reactive</u> they are.

Acid + Metal → Salt + Hydrogen

Here's the <u>typical experiment</u>:

1) The more <u>reactive</u> the metal, the <u>faster</u> the reaction will go — very reactive metals (e.g. sodium) react <u>explosively</u>.

2) The <u>speed</u> of reaction is indicated by the <u>rate</u> at which the <u>bubbles</u> of hydrogen are given off.

3) The <u>hydrogen</u> is confirmed by the <u>burning splint test</u> (see page 43).

Here are some examples:

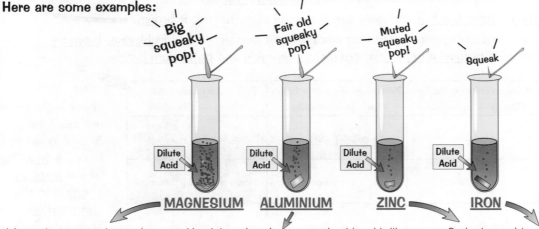

Magnesium reacts <u>vigorously</u> with <u>cold</u> dilute acids and produces <u>loads of bubbles</u>.

Aluminium doesn't react much with cold dilute acids because it has a protective aluminium oxide layer. But, it reacts <u>vigorously</u> with <u>warm</u> dilute acids and produces <u>a lot</u> of bubbles.

Both zinc and iron react <u>slowly</u> with dilute acids but more strongly if you heat them up.

The Name of the Salt Depends on the Metal and Acid Used

1) Metals <u>react</u> with dilute <u>hydrochloric acid</u> and <u>sulfuric acid</u> in the <u>same way</u>, but <u>different salts</u> are formed depending on the acid used.

2) <u>Hydrochloric acid</u> will always produce <u>chloride salts</u>.
   For example: hydrochloric acid + magnesium → magnesium chloride + hydrogen.

3) <u>Sulfuric acid</u> will always produce <u>sulfate salts</u>.
   For example: sulfuric acid + magnesium → magnesium sulfate + hydrogen.

Metals Also React with Water

The <u>reactions</u> of metals with <u>water</u> also show the reactivity of metals.

Metal + Water → Metal Hydroxide + Hydrogen
(Less reactive Metal + Steam → Metal oxide + Hydrogen)

1) Very reactive metals like <u>potassium</u>, <u>sodium</u>, <u>lithium</u> and <u>calcium</u> will all react <u>vigorously</u> with water.

2) Less reactive metals like <u>magnesium</u>, <u>zinc</u> and <u>iron</u> won't react much with cold water but they will react with <u>steam</u>.

3) <u>Copper</u> won't react with either water or steam.

Bubbles bubbles bubbles bubbles — I love the bubbles...

There's enough on this page to make the revision juices bubble more than a lump of potassium in a tube of dilute acid. If you react metals with water or dilute acid you'll get this order of reactivity from <u>most reactive</u> to <u>least reactive</u>: Potassium, Sodium, Lithium, Calcium, Magnesium, Zinc, Iron, Copper.

The Reactivity Series

The previous page covered some reactions that help you work out how <u>reactive</u> a <u>metal</u> is. You can use this information to put the metals in order of their <u>reactivity</u>. Which is more useful than it sounds, promise.

The <u>Reactivity Series</u> — <u>How Well</u> a <u>Metal</u> <u>Reacts</u>

The <u>reactivity series</u> lists metals in <u>order</u> of their <u>reactivity</u> towards other substances.

Make sure you learn this list:

The Reactivity Series

Potassium	K	Very Reactive
Sodium	Na	
Lithium	Li	
Calcium	Ca	
Magnesium	Mg	Fairly Reactive
Aluminium	Al	
Zinc	Zn	
Iron	Fe	Not very Reactive
Copper	Cu	
Silver	Ag	Not at all Reactive
Gold	Au	

A <u>More Reactive</u> <u>Metal</u> <u>Displaces</u> a <u>Less Reactive</u> <u>Metal</u>

1) <u>More reactive</u> metals react <u>more strongly</u> than <u>less reactive</u> metals.

2) This means that a more reactive metal will <u>displace</u> a less reactive metal from its oxide because it will bond <u>more strongly</u> to the oxygen.

> Example: <u>iron</u> would be displaced from <u>iron oxide</u> by the more reactive <u>aluminium</u>.
>
> iron oxide + aluminium → aluminium oxide + iron
> Fe_2O_3 + 2Al → Al_2O_3 + 2Fe

3) <u>Metal compounds</u> like copper sulfate, zinc chloride and sodium chloride are <u>metal salts</u>.

4) If you put a <u>reactive metal</u> into a solution of a <u>less reactive metal salt</u> the reactive metal will <u>replace</u> the <u>less reactive metal</u> in the salt.

> Example: put an <u>iron nail</u> in a solution of <u>copper sulfate</u> and the more reactive iron will "<u>kick out</u>" the less reactive copper from the salt. You end up with <u>iron sulfate solution</u> and <u>copper metal</u>.
>
> copper sulfate + iron → iron sulfate + copper
> $CuSO_4$ + Fe → $FeSO_4$ + Cu

5) If a piece of <u>silver metal</u> is put into a solution of copper sulfate, <u>nothing happens</u>. The more reactive metal (copper) is <u>already</u> in the salt.

6) You can use displacement reactions to <u>work out</u> where in the reactivity series a metal is supposed to go. For example, if you were given a lump of a mystery metal, you could try reacting it with different <u>metal oxides</u> and <u>salts</u>. If it <u>reacted</u> with copper oxide you'd know it was <u>higher</u> in the series than copper. If it <u>didn't react</u> with magnesium sulfate you'd know it was lower than magnesium in the reactivity series.

I AM NOT HIGHLY REACTIVE — OK...

If you're starting to wonder why any of this displacement stuff is important, let me tell you. Without it, we wouldn't be able to extract metals from ores, which means no <u>zinc</u> for making brass door handles, no <u>lead</u> for making lead-acid batteries and no <u>iron</u> filings to make amusing hairy face pictures with a magnet.

Iron

Iron's <u>strength</u> has made it a very important metal that's used throughout the world for <u>building construction</u>, <u>car manufacture</u> and wrought iron <u>garden furniture</u>. But the problem is — it rusts...

Iron and Steel _Corrode_ **to Make** _Rust_

1) Iron corrodes easily. In other words, it <u>rusts</u>. The word "rust" is only used for the corrosion of iron, not other metals.

2) Rusting only happens when the iron's in contact with both <u>oxygen</u> (from the air) and <u>water</u>.

3) The chemical reaction that takes place when iron corrodes is an <u>oxidation</u> reaction. The iron <u>gains oxygen</u> to form <u>iron(III) oxide</u>.

4) Water then becomes loosely bonded to the iron(III) oxide and the result is <u>hydrated iron(III) oxide</u> — which we call rust.

5) Learn the <u>word equation</u> for the reaction:

$$\text{iron} + \text{oxygen} + \text{water} \rightarrow \text{hydrated iron(III) oxide (rust)}$$

6) Unfortunately, rust is a soft crumbly solid that soon <u>flakes off</u> to leave more iron available to <u>rust again</u>.

There are _Two_ **Main Ways to** _Prevent Rusting_

1) The obvious way to prevent rusting is to <u>coat the iron</u> with a <u>barrier</u> to keep out the water and oxygen.

<u>BARRIER METHODS</u>:

> <u>Painting</u>/<u>Coating with plastic</u> — ideal for big and small structures alike. Can be decorative too.

> <u>Oiling</u>/<u>Greasing</u> — this has to be used when moving parts are involved, like on bike chains.

Jamie wanted to make sure his Nan didn't rust.

2) The other way is the <u>sacrificial method</u>. This involves placing a <u>more reactive metal</u> with the iron. The water and oxygen then react with this sacrificial metal <u>instead</u> of with the iron.

- <u>Zinc</u> is often used as a sacrificial metal.
- The zinc is <u>more reactive</u> than iron — it's further up the reactivity series.
- So, the zinc will be oxidised <u>instead</u> of the iron.
- A <u>coating of zinc</u> can be sprayed onto the object — this is known as <u>galvanising</u>.
- Or big <u>blocks of zinc</u> can be bolted to the iron. This is used on ships' hulls, or on underground iron pipes.

The sacrificial method — who knew chemistry could sound so bloodthirsty...

So there you have it folks. If you've wondered how Iron Man avoids rusting, it's a combination of greasing himself up and sending out Zinc Man if it's raining. Make sure you learn all the stuff on this page by <u>covering</u> the page and <u>writing it all out again</u> — not that you need me to remind you of the method of course...

Oxygen in the Atmosphere

This page is all about oxygen — what a breath of fresh air...

The Atmosphere is Mostly Nitrogen and Oxygen

For 200 million years or so, the atmosphere has been about how it is now:

78% NITROGEN

nearly 1% ARGON

21% OXYGEN

only 0.04% CO_2

There can be a lot of water vapour too.

Make sure you know the proportions of each gas.

You Can Investigate the Proportion of Oxygen in the Atmosphere

Here are a couple of nice experiments that show that the atmosphere today contains around one fifth oxygen.

Using Copper

You need to make sure that the system is sealed so no extra air can get in and out.

1) When it's heated, copper reacts with oxygen in the air to make copper(II) oxide — so the reaction uses up oxygen.

2) If you heat an excess of copper in a tube and pass air over it using two syringes, you can use the markers on the syringes to tell how much oxygen has been used up.

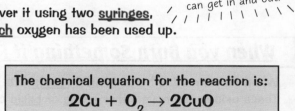

Copper

Air

Heat

The chemical equation for the reaction is:
$$2Cu + O_2 \rightarrow 2CuO$$

3) If you start with 100 cm³ of air, you'll end up with about 80 cm³ when the reaction's finished and the air has cooled. If 20 cm³ of air has gone then around 20% of the air must be oxygen.

Using Iron or Phosphorus

1) Iron reacts with oxygen in the air to form rust (see page 36) — so iron will remove oxygen from the air.

2) To do this experiment, first soak some iron wool in acetic acid (the acid will catalyse the reaction). Then push the wool into a test tube, put your thumb over the end and invert the tube into a beaker of water.

3) Over time, the level of the water in the test tube will rise.

4) This is because the iron reacts with the oxygen in the air to make iron oxide. The water rises to fill the space the oxygen took up.

5) To work out the percentage of the air that is oxygen you need to mark the starting and finishing position of the water.

6) Then, fill the tube up to each mark with water and pour the contents into a measuring cylinder to find out the volume of air at the start and the end.

7) Use the difference between the start and end volumes to work out the percentage of the starting volume that has been used up — it should be about 20%.

8) You can do a similar experiment with white phosphorus. White phosphorus smoulders in air to produce phosphorus oxide. Calculate the amount of oxygen in the air in the same way as for iron.

Iron wool

Finishing position of water.

Starting position of water.

Water

Pump those gas syringes...

I think using those syringes is a clever way of calculating how much oxygen is in the air — and you can give your thumbs a work out at the same time. Make sure you learn the method using iron or phosphorus too though.

Oxygen in Reactions

This page has lots of reactions involving oxygen. You need to learn how to prepare it in the lab and how it reacts with other elements to form oxides — more commonly known as "what happens when you burn something".

You can Make O_2 in the Lab

1) Making pure oxygen in the lab is a cinch. It's made from hydrogen peroxide (H_2O_2).
2) The hydrogen peroxide will decompose (break apart) into water and oxygen. Here's the equation:

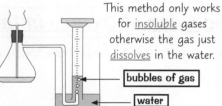

$$2H_2O_{2\,(aq)} \rightarrow 2H_2O_{(l)} + O_{2\,(g)}$$

3) This decomposition is really slow but the rate of the reaction can be increased with a sprinkle of manganese(IV) oxide catalyst. The catalyst speeds the reaction up without being used up itself.
4) You can collect the oxygen that's produced over water or by using a gas syringe:

COLLECTION OVER WATER
You can use a delivery tube to bubble the gas into an upside-down measuring cylinder or gas jar filled with water.

This method only works for insoluble gases otherwise the gas just dissolves in the water.

bubbles of gas
water

GAS SYRINGE
You can use a gas syringe to collect pretty much any gas.

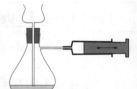

When you Burn Something it Reacts with Oxygen in Air

When an element is burnt in air it reacts with the oxygen to form an oxide. These oxides can have either acidic or basic character.

Here are some examples you need to know:

Magnesium

Magnesium burns with a bright white flame in air and the white powder that is formed is magnesium oxide. Magnesium oxide is slightly alkaline when it's dissolved in water.

$$2Mg_{(s)} + O_{2(g)} \rightarrow 2MgO_{(s)}$$

Carbon

Carbon will burn in air if it's very strongly heated. It has an orangey/yellowy flame and it produces carbon dioxide gas. Carbon dioxide is slightly acidic when it's dissolved in water.

$$C_{(s)} + O_{2(g)} \rightarrow CO_{2(g)}$$

Sulfur

Sulfur burns in air or oxygen with a pale blue flame and produces sulfur dioxide. Sulfur dioxide is acidic when it's dissolved in water.

$$S_{(s)} + O_{2(g)} \rightarrow SO_{2(g)}$$

It's a good job they don't make park benches out of magnesium...

There's quite a bit to remember on this page. You need to learn how to make O_2 from hydrogen peroxide and how oxygen reacts with magnesium, carbon and sulfur. And, if that wasn't enough, you need to know whether magnesium oxide, carbon dioxide and sulfur dioxide react with water to make an acidic or alkaline solution.

Preparation of Carbon Dioxide

Here are two ways of producing CO_2 in the lab — and you need to know about both of them.
But first, a bit of detail on some more methods of collecting gases...

You Can Collect Gases in a Test Tube

You can collect gases inside a test tube full of air. This works because the gas you're collecting displaces the air in the tube. There are two ways that this can be done: upward delivery and downward delivery.

UPWARD / DOWNWARD DELIVERY

This all depends on the density of the gas relative to the density of air.
1) The delivery tube is fed directly into a test tube either upwards or downwards.
2) Use upward delivery to collect 'lighter than air' gases (e.g. H_2).
3) Use downward delivery to collect 'heavier than air' gases (e.g. CO_2, Cl_2).

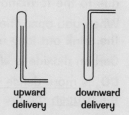
upward delivery   downward delivery

Dilute Acid reacts with Calcium Carbonate to Produce Carbon Dioxide

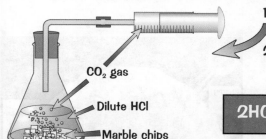
CO₂ gas
Dilute HCl
Marble chips

1) The calcium carbonate (marble chips) is put in the bottom of a flask and dilute hydrochloric acid is added.
2) The dilute HCl reacts with the calcium carbonate to produce calcium chloride, water and carbon dioxide gas.

$$2HCl_{(aq)} + CaCO_{3(s)} \rightarrow CaCl_{2(aq)} + H_2O_{(l)} + CO_{2(g)}$$

hydrochloric acid + calcium carbonate → calcium chloride + water + carbon dioxide

3) The carbon dioxide gas is collected in a gas syringe or using downward delivery (see above).

The Thermal Decomposition of Metal Carbonates Also Produces CO_2

1) Another way of making CO_2 is by heating a metal carbonate.
2) This is an example of thermal decomposition, which is when a substance breaks down into simpler substances when heated.
3) Copper(II) carbonate is a green powder that will easily decompose to form carbon dioxide and copper(II) oxide when you heat it.
4) Here's the equation for the thermal decomposition of copper(II) carbonate:

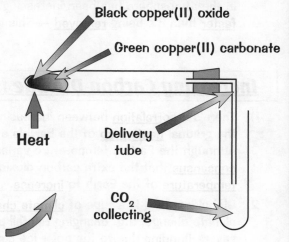
Black copper(II) oxide
Green copper(II) carbonate
Heat
Delivery tube
CO₂ collecting

$$CuCO_{3(s)} \rightarrow CuO_{(s)} + CO_{2(g)}$$

copper(II) carbonate → copper oxide + carbon dioxide

5) To do the experiment, heat copper(II) carbonate then collect the gas that's given off using the downward delivery method.

Upward delivery — midwives advise against it...

There are a couple more ways to collect gases here — upward and downward delivery. Just make sure you use the right one or the gas will escape. The CO_2 making stuff isn't so bad either, and if you're wondering how it's helpful in life, then using acid to release CO_2 is how baking powder makes your cakes rise — and we all love cakes that rise.

Carbon Dioxide — the Good and the Bad

Carbon dioxide has some <u>uses</u> but it can cause a few <u>problems</u> too...

CO₂ is used in Fizzy Drinks and Fire Extinguishers

1) CO₂ is used in <u>carbonated drinks</u> to make them fizzzzzzzzzzzzzzz.

2) The CO₂ is <u>slightly soluble</u> in water and dissolves into the drinks when under pressure. This produces a <u>slightly acidic solution</u> due to the formation of <u>carbonic acid</u>.

$$CO_{2(g)} + H_2O_{(l)} \rightarrow H_2CO_{3(aq)}$$

carbon dioxide + water → carbonic acid

3) When you open the bottle the <u>bubbles</u> are the CO₂ <u>escaping</u>. If you leave the drink out long enough it will go flat because all the CO₂ escapes.

4) Carbon dioxide is also used in <u>fire extinguishers</u>.

5) CO₂ is <u>more dense than air</u> — so it <u>sinks</u> onto the flames and <u>stops</u> the <u>oxygen</u> the fire needs getting to it.

6) Carbon dioxide fire extinguishers are used when water extinguishers <u>aren't</u> safe, for example when putting out <u>electrical fires</u>.

Is that a really big bottle or a really small extinguisher?

Carbon Dioxide is a Greenhouse Gas

1) The <u>temperature</u> of the Earth is a <u>balance</u> between the heat it gets from the Sun and the heat it radiates back out into space.

2) Gases in the <u>atmosphere</u> like <u>carbon dioxide</u>, <u>methane</u> and <u>water vapour</u> naturally act like an <u>insulating layer</u>. They are often called 'greenhouse gases'. They absorb most of the heat that would normally be radiated out into space, and re-radiate it in all directions — including back towards the Earth.

3) <u>Human activity</u> affects the <u>amount of carbon dioxide</u> in the atmosphere — examples include:

- <u>Deforestation</u>: fewer trees means less CO₂ is removed from the atmosphere via photosynthesis.
- <u>Burning fossil fuels</u>: carbon that was 'locked up' in these fuels is being released as CO₂.

4) It is because of this human activity that over the last 200 years or so, the concentration of carbon dioxide in the atmosphere has been increasing. For this to have happened, CO₂ must be being <u>released</u> into the air <u>faster</u> than it's being <u>removed</u> — this is linked to climate change (see below).

Increasing Carbon Dioxide is Linked to Climate Change

1) There's a <u>correlation</u> between increasing levels of carbon dioxide and the gradual <u>heating up</u> of the Earth's atmosphere (<u>global warming</u>). Although the Earth's temperature varies naturally, there's a <u>scientific consensus</u> that the extra carbon dioxide has <u>caused</u> the average <u>temperature</u> of the Earth to <u>increase</u>.

2) Global warming is a type of <u>climate change</u> and causes other types of climate change, e.g. changing rainfall patterns. It could also cause severe <u>flooding</u> due to the polar ice caps melting and <u>sea level rise</u>.

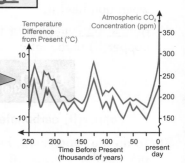

Eee, problems, problems — there's always summat goin' wrong...

<u>Carbon dioxide</u> is a real pain — not only does it contribute to <u>global climate change</u> but it makes bubbles go up your nose when you're drinking fizzy pop. How rude. Learn all of this page by covering it up and then writing everything out. Keep going 'till you can get it all, then risk the bubbles and have a lemonade to celebrate.

Tests for Cations

Forensic science involves a lot of <u>chemical tests</u>, which is what these next pages are about.
Before you start reading, you have to pretend you have a <u>mystery substance</u>. You don't know what it is, but you need to find out — just like that bloke off the telly who investigates murders.

First off, some tests for <u>cations</u> (positive ions — such as Na^+ or Ca^{2+}).

Flame Tests <u>Identify</u> <u>Metal Ions</u>

Compounds of some metals burn with a <u>characteristic colour</u> (as you see every November 5th).

So you can test for various metal ions by heating your substance
and seeing whether it <u>burns</u> with a <u>distinctive colour flame</u>.

> <u>Lithium</u>, Li^+, burns with a crimson-red flame.
>
> <u>Sodium</u>, Na^+, burns with an yellow-orange flame.
>
> <u>Potassium</u>, K^+, burns with a lilac flame.
>
> <u>Calcium</u>, Ca^{2+}, burns with a brick-red flame.

To do the test you need to <u>clean</u> a <u>platinum</u> wire loop by dipping it in some dilute <u>HCl</u> and then holding it in a <u>flame</u>. Once you hold the loop in the flame and it burns <u>without any colour</u> you can dip it into the <u>sample</u> you want to test, then put it back in the flame. Then say ooooo and ahhhhh.

<u>Some</u> <u>Metals</u> <u>Form a</u> <u>Coloured Precipitate</u> <u>with</u> NaOH

This is also a test for metal ions, but it's slightly more involved. Concentrate now...

1) Many <u>metal hydroxides</u> are <u>insoluble</u> and precipitate out of solution when formed.
   Some of these hydroxides have a <u>characteristic colour</u>.

2) So in this test you add a few drops of <u>sodium hydroxide</u> solution to a solution of your mystery compound in a test tube — all in the hope of forming an insoluble hydroxide.

3) If you get a <u>coloured insoluble hydroxide</u> you can then tell which metal was in the compound.

Metal ion	Colour of precipitate	Ionic Reaction
Copper(II), Cu^{2+}	Blue	$Cu^{2+}(aq) + 2OH^-(aq) \rightarrow Cu(OH)_2(s)$
Iron(II), Fe^{2+}	Sludgy green	$Fe^{2+}(aq) + 2OH^-(aq) \rightarrow Fe(OH)_2(s)$
Iron(III), Fe^{3+}	Reddish brown	$Fe^{3+}(aq) + 3OH^-(aq) \rightarrow Fe(OH)_3(s)$

"Ammonium Compound + NaOH" Gives Off (Stinky) Ammonia

1) <u>Ammonia gas</u> (NH_3) is smelly — it reeks of <u>cat wee</u>. You can usually tell if there's some about, but it's not a good idea to smell it deliberately as it can be really <u>harmful to your eyes</u> — not cool.

2) You can <u>check for ammonia gas</u> using a damp piece of <u>red litmus paper</u>.
   If there's ammonia present, the paper will turn <u>blue</u>.

3) You can use this to <u>test</u> whether a substance contains <u>ammonium ions</u> (NH_4^+). Add some <u>sodium hydroxide</u> to a solution of your mystery substance in a test tube. If there's ammonia given off this means there are ammonium ions in your mystery substance.

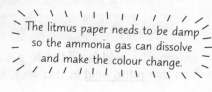

The litmus paper needs to be damp so the ammonia gas can dissolve and make the colour change.

The Ammonia Mystery — smells like my cat did it...

Remember... your <u>cation</u> is your <u>metal ion</u>, and <u>cations</u> are <u>positive</u> — they'd be attracted to a <u>cathode</u> (which is negative, remember). Now these tests assume that your mystery substance is <u>ionic</u>, which of course it might not be. But you might be able to tell — ionic substances tend to be <u>crystalline solids</u> with a high melting point. So, if it's a gas, a volatile liquid (you might be able to smell it) or a soft solid, no need to bother with these tests.

42

Tests for Anions

It's not just positive ions you can test for, you'll be pleased to know.
Yep, you can also test for negative ions. So the fun goes on...

Hydrochloric Acid Can Help Detect Carbonates

To test for carbonates, add dilute hydrochloric acid (HCl) to your test sample.
If carbonates (CO_3^{2-}) are present then carbon dioxide will be released.

> ### Carbonates give off CO_2 with HCl

$$CO_3^{2-}{}_{(s)} + 2H^+{}_{(aq)} \rightarrow CO_{2(g)} + H_2O_{(l)}$$

carbonate + acid → carbon dioxide + water

You can test for carbon dioxide using limewater — see page 43.

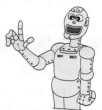

If you're wondering how this picture of a robot relates to carbonates and acids you aren't alone.

Test for Sulfates with HCl and Barium Chloride

> ### Sulfate ions (SO_4^{2-}) produce a white precipitate

To test for a sulfate ion (SO_4^{2-}), add dilute HCl, followed by barium chloride solution, $BaCl_2$.

$$Ba^{2+}{}_{(aq)} + SO_4^{2-}{}_{(aq)} \rightarrow BaSO_{4(s)}$$

A white precipitate of barium sulfate means the original compound was a sulfate.

(The hydrochloric acid is added to get rid of any traces of carbonate or sulfite ions before you do the test. Both of these would also produce a precipitate, so they'd confuse the results.)

Test for Halides (Cl^-, Br^-, I^-) with Nitric Acid and Silver Nitrate

To test for chloride, bromide or iodide ions, add dilute nitric acid (HNO_3), followed by silver nitrate solution ($AgNO_3$).

$$Ag^+{}_{(aq)} + Cl^-{}_{(aq)} \longrightarrow AgCl_{(s)}$$ — A chloride ion gives a white precipitate of silver chloride.

$$Ag^+{}_{(aq)} + Br^-{}_{(aq)} \longrightarrow AgBr_{(s)}$$ — A bromide ion gives a cream precipitate of silver bromide.

$$Ag^+{}_{(aq)} + I^-{}_{(aq)} \longrightarrow AgI_{(s)}$$ — An iodide ion gives a yellow precipitate of silver iodide.

(Again, the acid is added to get rid of carbonate or sulfite ions before the test.
You use nitric acid in this test, though, not HCl.)

These tests just detect negative ions — not happy cheery ones...

How to learn this page — don't stare at the whole thing till your eyes swim and you don't want to see the word "precipitate" ever again. It's been handily divided into three subsections, so learn it that way.
Take the 'acid test' first, then the sulfates, then the halides. Cover up the page and see what you know.

Section 2 — Chemistry of the Elements

Tests for Gases and Water

There are lots of clever ways of testing for <u>different gases</u>. But dipping your finger in a liquid and saying "<u>it's wet</u>" is <u>not</u> the best test for water. Don't worry though, there's a more scientific method for that too...

There are Tests for 5 Common Gases

1) Chlorine — Chlorine <u>bleaches</u> damp <u>litmus paper</u>, turning it white. (It may turn <u>red</u> for a moment first though — that's because a solution of chlorine is <u>acidic</u>.)

Damp litmus paper

2) Oxygen — Oxygen <u>relights</u> a <u>glowing splint</u>.

Glowing splint

3) Carbon Dioxide — Carbon dioxide <u>turns limewater cloudy</u> — just bubble the gas through a test tube of limewater and watch what happens.

CO_2 gas
Limewater

4) Hydrogen — Hydrogen makes a "<u>squeaky pop</u>" with a <u>lighted splint</u>. (The noise comes from the hydrogen burning with the oxygen in the air to form H_2O.)

Squeaky pop!
Squeaky pop!

5) Ammonia — Ammonia <u>turns</u> damp <u>red litmus paper blue</u>. (It also has a very strong <u>smell</u>.)

Wet Copper(II) Sulfate is Blue — Dry Copper(II) Sulfate is White

<u>Copper(II) sulfate</u> crystals can be used as a <u>test</u> for <u>water</u>.

1) When copper(II) sulfate is <u>bound to water</u> (water of crystallisation, see page 22) it forms lovely <u>blue crystals</u>.

2) If you <u>heat</u> the <u>blue hydrated</u> copper(II) sulfate crystals it drives the water off.

3) This leaves a <u>white anhydrous</u> copper(II) sulfate powder, which <u>doesn't</u> have any water bound to it.

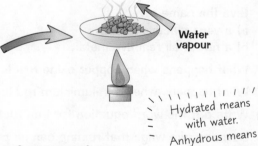
Water vapour

Hydrated means with water. Anhydrous means without water.

4) If you then <u>add</u> a couple of drops of <u>water</u> to the <u>white powder</u> you get the <u>blue crystals</u> back again.

So, if you want to <u>test for water</u>, all you need to do is add <u>anhydrous copper(II) sulfate</u> and see if the white powder turns blue.

This test <u>will</u> tell you if water is <u>present</u> in a solution but it <u>won't</u> tell you if the water is <u>pure</u>.

- When a sample is <u>pure</u> it means it's only made up of <u>one substance</u>.
- This means it has set <u>defined physical properties</u> like <u>boiling point</u> and <u>freezing point</u>.

<u>Pure water</u> will always: Boil at 100 °C
Freeze at 0 °C

If you find the boiling point isn't 100 °C or freezing point isn't 0 °C then the sample <u>isn't pure</u>.

So there's a test for water — that's really whet my appetite for chemistry...

So, if you want to test for <u>chlorine</u> or <u>ammonia</u> you need litmus paper, for <u>oxygen</u> or <u>hydrogen</u> you need a splint, and for <u>carbon dioxide</u> you need limewater. Oh and if you want to know if water is present in a solution just add anhydrous copper(II) sulfate. If the white crystals turn blue then there's water and if they don't there isn't.

Revision Summary for Section 2

It's the end of the section, which can mean only one thing — it's quiz time. Below are a wonderful selection of questions designed to make sure all the important info sticks in your brain better than breakfast cereal that's been left to dry in a bowl. If you find yourself struggling with a few of the questions then flick back to the appropriate page and have another read. Keep going 'til you can do them all.

1) What are the rows on the periodic table called? What are the columns on the periodic table called?

2) Why are the noble gases inert?

3) Name the gas that is produced when an alkali metal reacts with water.

4) Write the word equation for the reaction between sodium and water.

5) Describe how the reactivity of alkali metals changes as you go down the group.

6) How does the boiling point of the halogens change as the atomic number increases?

7) Describe how the reactivity of the halogens changes as you go up the group.

8) What's hydrogen chloride called when it's in aqueous solution?

9) Describe what happens when hydrogen chloride is added to water. What is this process called?

10) Explain why HCl in methylbenzene is not acidic.

11) What is a displacement reaction?

12) If you mix chlorine water with potassium bromide solution, what colour will it go?

13) If you mix bromine water with potassium iodide solution, what colour will it go?

14) What does OIL RIG stand for?

15) Write the word equation for the reaction of an acid with a metal.

16) Put these metals in order from most reactive to least reactive when added to dilute acid: aluminium, iron, magnesium and zinc.

17) Give the name of:
    a) a very reactive metal,
    b) a not at all reactive metal.

18)* What happens when copper oxide reacts with magnesium?

19)* What happens when an aluminium rod is put in a solution of zinc sulfate?

20) Write out the word equation for iron rusting.

21) Describe two ways that rusting can be prevented.

22) What percentage of the atmosphere is oxygen?

23) Describe an experiment to prepare oxygen that can be carried out in a lab.

24) Describe the reaction of oxygen with magnesium.

25) Give two ways of preparing carbon dioxide in the lab.

26) Give two uses of carbon dioxide.

27) Explain the link between carbon dioxide and global warming.

28) What colour flame does potassium burn with?

29) What colour precipitate do iron(II) compounds form with sodium hydroxide?

30) Give the name of an acid which can be used to test for the presence of carbonate ions.

31) What colour is the precipitate formed when a bromide ion reacts with dilute nitric acid and silver nitrate?

32) What is the test for carbon dioxide?

33) What is the test for hydrogen gas?

34) What colour are the crystals of hydrated copper(II) sulfate that form in the presence of water?

35) How can you tell if a sample of water is pure?

* Answers on page 84.

Alkanes

A new page and a new section. This one's a diddy little thing that's all about **organic chemistry**. That just means it's about molecules that contain **carbon**.

Alkanes are Hydrocarbons

1) **Hydrocarbons** are molecules that are made up of **hydrogen** and **carbon** atoms **only**.

2) Alkanes are hydrocarbons — they're **chains of carbon atoms** surrounded by **hydrogen atoms** like this.

3) Different alkanes have chains of different **lengths**.

4) You need to know the **names** and the **displayed formulas** of the first five alkanes.

$$H-C-C-C-C-H$$

> The displayed formula is a picture of the molecule drawn with all the bonds shown.

1) Methane
Formula: CH_4

$$H-C-H$$

(natural gas)

2) Ethane
Formula: C_2H_6

$$H-C-C-H$$

3) Propane
Formula: C_3H_8

$$H-C-C-C-H$$

4) Butane
Formula: C_4H_{10}

$$H-C-C-C-C-H$$

5) Pentane
Formula: C_5H_{12}

$$H-C-C-C-C-C-H$$

> To help remember the names of the first four alkanes just remember: Mice Eat Peanut Butter. Pentane is five, just like a pentagon, so you'll have to remember that one on its own.

Alkanes are a Homologous Series

1) The alkanes above are part of a **homologous series**.

2) A homologous series is a **group of compounds** that can all be represented by the **same general formula**.

3) You can use a general formula to work out the **molecular formula** of **any member** of a homologous series.

4) Alkanes all have the **general formula**:

$$\text{Alkanes} = C_nH_{2n+2}$$

5) So if an alkane has **4 carbons** (butane), it's got to have $(2\times4)+2 = $ **10 hydrogens**.

6) A carbon atom can form **four covalent bonds** and a hydrogen atom can only form **one covalent bond** (see pages 12-13). The diagrams of the alkanes above show that all the carbon atoms have formed four bonds and all the hydrogen atoms have formed one bond — a line represents each covalent bond.

7) No more atoms can join onto the carbon atoms so the alkanes are **saturated**.

Alkane ya if you don't learn this...

Only joking... but the stuff on this page is pretty important, so make sure you've got your head around it before you turn over. That general formula might look a bit scary, but once you've learnt it you'll be able to work out the molecular formula of any alkane. Which may come in handy if, say, you're asked to draw one in an exam...

More Alkanes

We get loads of alkanes from oil. And then we burn them. But there's <u>burning</u> and there's <u>burning</u>...

Complete Combustion *Happens When There's Plenty of* Oxygen

When there's <u>plenty of oxygen</u> about, alkanes burn to produce <u>carbon dioxide</u> and <u>water</u>.

Lots of CO_2 isn't ideal, but the alternatives are worse (see below).

$$\text{alkane} + \text{oxygen} \longrightarrow \text{carbon dioxide} + \text{water} \quad (+ \text{ energy})$$

1) <u>Complete combustion</u> releases <u>lots of energy</u> and only produces those two <u>harmless waste products</u>. When there's <u>plenty of oxygen</u> and combustion is complete, the gas burns with a <u>clean blue flame</u>.

2) Here's the <u>balanced equation</u> for the complete combustion of <u>methane</u>, a <u>hydrocarbon fuel</u>.

$$CH_4 + 2O_2 \rightarrow CO_2 + 2H_2O$$

Make sure you end up with the <u>same number</u> of Cs, Hs and Os on <u>either side</u> of the arrow.

3) Many <u>heaters</u> that burn <u>methane</u> (natural gas) release the <u>waste gases</u> into the room, which is perfectly OK. As long as the gas heater is <u>working properly</u> and the room is <u>well ventilated</u>, there's no problem.

Incomplete Combustion *of Alkanes is* NOT Safe

1) If there <u>isn't enough oxygen</u>, alkane combustion will be <u>incomplete</u>. Carbon dioxide and water are still produced, but you can also get <u>carbon</u> and <u>carbon monoxide</u> (CO), which is a poisonous gas (see p. 71).

$$\text{alkane} + \text{oxygen} \longrightarrow \text{carbon} + \text{carbon monoxide} + \text{carbon dioxide} + \text{water}$$

$$(+ \text{ energy})$$

2) Incomplete combustion means a <u>smoky yellow flame</u>, and <u>less energy</u> than complete combustion.

3) Here's an example of an <u>equation</u> for incomplete combustion.

$$4CH_4 + 6O_2 \rightarrow C + 2CO + CO_2 + 8H_2O$$

This is just <u>one possibility</u>. The products depend on how much oxygen is present...

... e.g. you could also have: $4CH_4 + 7O_2 \rightarrow 2CO + 2CO_2 + 8H_2O$ — but the equation has to be <u>balanced</u>.

Halogens *React with* Alkanes *to make* Haloalkanes

1) <u>Chlorine</u> and <u>bromine</u> react with alkanes in the presence of <u>ultraviolet light</u>.

2) In these reactions a <u>hydrogen</u> atom from the alkane is <u>substituted</u> (replaced) by <u>chlorine</u> or <u>bromine</u>. So this is called a <u>substitution reaction</u>.

3) This is how bromine and methane react together to form <u>bromomethane</u>.

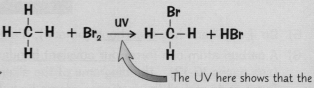

methane + bromine → bromomethane + hydrogen bromide

$$H-\overset{\overset{\displaystyle H}{|}}{\underset{\underset{\displaystyle H}{|}}{C}}-H + Br_2 \xrightarrow{\text{UV}} H-\overset{\overset{\displaystyle Br}{|}}{\underset{\underset{\displaystyle H}{|}}{C}}-H + HBr$$

The UV here shows that the reaction needs ultraviolet light.

Blue flame good, orange flame bad...

Alkanes are often used as fuels. An ideal fuel would be <u>easy to ignite</u>, produce <u>no soot</u> or <u>toxic products</u>, release <u>loads of energy</u> and be capable of being <u>stored safely</u>. There should also be a <u>cheap</u> and <u>sustainable supply</u> of it. Alkanes don't tick all these boxes but in reality, you have to go for the <u>best compromise</u>.

Alkenes

Alkenes are another type of hydrocarbon. They're different from alkanes because they contain <u>double bonds</u>.

Alkenes **Have a** C=C Double Bond

1) Alkenes are hydrocarbons which have a <u>double bond</u> between two of the <u>carbon</u> atoms in their chain.
2) They are <u>unsaturated</u> molecules because they <u>can make more bonds</u> — the double bond can open up, allowing the two carbon atoms to bond with other atoms (see below).
3) The first three alkenes are <u>ethene</u> (with two carbon atoms) <u>propene</u> (three Cs) and <u>butene</u> (four Cs).
4) <u>All alkenes</u> have the general formula: C_nH_{2n} — they have twice as many hydrogens as carbons.

$$\text{Alkenes} = C_nH_{2n}$$

1) Ethene
Formula: C_2H_4

Hydrogen atoms only make one bond.

This is a double bond — so each carbon atom is still making four bonds.

2) Propene
Formula: C_3H_6

3) Butene
Formula: C_4H_8

There are <u>two</u> different structures for butene (C_4H_8) — the double bond can be in two different places. When two molecules have <u>identical molecular formulas</u> but <u>different structures</u> they are called <u>isomers</u>.

Halogens **React with** Alkenes, **Forming** Haloalkanes

1) <u>Halogens</u> can react with alkenes to make <u>haloalkanes</u>.
2) For example bromine and ethene react together to form <u>dibromoethane</u>.
3) These are called <u>addition reactions</u> because the C=C double bond is split and a halogen atom is <u>added</u> to each of the carbons.

There are two bromine atoms so it's called <u>dibromoethane</u>.

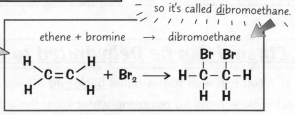

ethene + bromine → dibromoethane

- The reaction between bromine and alkenes is often used as a <u>test</u> for carbon-carbon double bonds.
- When you shake an alkene with <u>orange bromine water</u>, the solution becomes <u>colourless</u> — this is because the <u>bromine</u> molecules, which are <u>orange</u>, are reacting with the <u>alkene</u> to make a <u>dibromoalkane</u>, which is <u>colourless</u>.

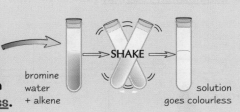

bromine water + alkene → SHAKE → solution goes colourless

Hallo alkane — a nice way to greet dibromoethane...

Don't get alkenes confused with alkanes — that one letter makes all the difference. Alkenes have a C=C bond, alkanes don't. But the first part of both their names tells you how many C atoms they have. "<u>Meth-</u>" means "<u>one</u> carbon atom", "<u>eth-</u>" means "<u>two</u> C atoms", "<u>prop-</u>" means "<u>three</u> C atoms", "<u>but-</u>" means "<u>four</u> C atoms".

Ethanol

The best way to make ethanol often depends on which resource is most easily available — oil or sugar.

Ethanol Can Be Produced from Ethene and Steam

1) Ethene is produced from crude oil (by cracking — see page 72).

2) Ethene (C_2H_4) will react with steam (H_2O) to make ethanol.

3) The reaction needs a temperature of 300°C and a pressure of 60-70 atmospheres.

4) Phosphoric acid is used as a catalyst.

5) At the moment this is a cheap process, because ethene's fairly cheap and not much of it is wasted.

6) The trouble is that crude oil is a non-renewable resource, which will start running out fairly soon. This means that using ethene to make ethanol will become very expensive.

$$C_2H_4 + H_2O \rightarrow C_2H_5OH$$

Ethanol Can Also Be Produced by Fermentation

The alcohol in beer and wine etc. isn't made from ethene — it's made by fermentation.

1) The raw material for fermentation is sugar e.g. glucose. This is converted into ethanol using yeast.

2) This process needs a lower temperature (about 30°C) and simpler equipment than when using ethene.

3) Another advantage is that the raw materials are all renewable resources. Sugar (sugar cane) is grown as a major crop in several parts of the world, including many poorer countries. Yeast is also easy to grow.

4) There are disadvantages though. The ethanol you get from this process isn't very concentrated, so it needs to be distilled to increase its strength (as in whisky distilleries). It also needs to be purified.

Both Methods have Advantages and Disadvantages...

You need to know the factors that affect which method you use to produce ethanol. Here's a quick summary:

Method	Rate of reaction	Quality of product	Raw material	Process/Costs
Ethene + steam	Very fast	Pure	Ethene from oil — a finite resource	Continuous process at high temp and pressure, so expensive equipment needed, but low labour costs.
Fermentation	Very slow	Very impure — needs further processing	Sugar — a renewable resource	Batch process at lower temp, so cheap equipment needed, but high labour costs.

Ethanol can be Dehydrated to Form Ethene

1) You can also turn ethanol back into ethene.

2) This is done by removing water from the ethanol in a dehydration reaction (i.e. elimination of water).

$$C_2H_5OH \rightarrow C_2H_4 + H_2O$$

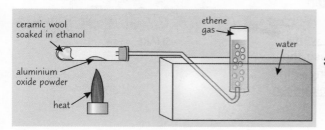

ceramic wool soaked in ethanol
ethene gas
water
aluminium oxide powder
heat

3) Ethanol vapour is passed over a hot catalyst of aluminium oxide, Al_2O_3 — the catalyst provides a large surface area for the reaction.

Make ethanol — not war...

Make sure you learn all the reactions on these pages. You need to know the conditions for the two different ways of manufacturing ethanol and what the benefits of each method are. So, cover the page and write it all out.

Revision Summary for Section 3

What?... Is that it?... Blimey, that section was short and sweet. Oh well, I guess that means you've got to the revision questions nice and quickly. But don't think that just because there are only four pages of stuff to learn I'm gonna go easy on you. Oh no. Each of these questions is carefully crafted to make sure you really did read all of those four pages. Keep trying till you can do them all without having to look back at the section.

1) What type of molecule is an alkane?

2) What is the name of this alkane?

$$H-\overset{\displaystyle H}{\underset{\displaystyle H}{C}}-\overset{\displaystyle H}{\underset{\displaystyle H}{C}}-H$$

3) Draw the displayed formula of propane.

4) What is a homologous series?

5) What is the general formula for alkanes?

6) What does saturated mean?

7) Write out the word equation for the complete combustion of an alkane.

8) Write out the balanced equation for the complete combustion of methane.

9) Write out the word equation for the incomplete combustion of an alkane.

10) Does complete or incomplete combustion produce more energy?

11) What is needed to start the reaction between a halogen and an alkane?

12) a) Write out the equation for the reaction between methane and bromine in the presence of UV light.

   b) Give the names of the products of this reaction.

13) What is the main feature of an alkene?

14) Explain why alkenes are known as unsaturated molecules?

15) What is the general formula of an alkene?

16) What's the name of this alkene?

$$H-\overset{\displaystyle H}{\underset{\displaystyle H}{C}}-\overset{\displaystyle H}{C}=C\overset{\displaystyle H}{\underset{\displaystyle H}{<}}$$

17) Draw the two possible structures of butene.

18) What is the name given to two molecules with identical molecular formulas but different structures?

19) What's the name of the type of reaction that happens between a halogen and an alkene?

20) a) Write out the equation for the reaction between ethene and bromine.

   b) Explain how you can use this reaction to test for carbon-carbon double bonds.

21) a) Write out the equation for the reaction between ethene and steam to make ethanol.

   b) What temperature and pressure does this reaction need?

   c) What is the catalyst that's used for this reaction?

22) a) In fermentation, what converts the sugar into ethanol?

   b) What temperature does this reaction need?

23) a) Write out the equation for the dehydration of ethanol to make ethene.

   b) What is the catalyst that's used for this reaction?

Acids and Alkalis

To test the pH of a solution, you can use an <u>indicator</u> — and that means <u>colours</u>...

The pH Scale Goes from 0 to 14

1) The <u>strongest acid</u> has <u>pH 0</u>. The <u>strongest alkali</u> has <u>pH 14</u>.

2) A <u>neutral</u> substance has <u>pH 7</u> (e.g. pure water).

| Strongly acidic | | | | | Weakly acidic | | | | Weakly alkaline | | | | | Strongly alkaline |

pH 0   1   2   3   4   5   6   7   8   9   10   11   12   13   14

ACIDS   NEUTRAL   ALKALIS

- car battery acid, stomach acid
- vinegar, lemon juice
- acid rain
- normal rain
- pure water
- washing-up liquid
- pancreatic juice
- soap powder
- bleach
- caustic soda (drain cleaner)

An Indicator is Just a Dye That Changes Colour

The dye in the indicator <u>changes colour</u> depending on whether it's <u>above</u> or <u>below</u> a <u>certain pH</u>. Indicators are very useful for <u>estimating</u> the pH of a solution. There are several different types:

1) <u>Universal indicator</u> is a very useful <u>combination of dyes</u> which gives the colours shown above.

2) <u>Litmus paper</u> tests whether a solution is acidic or alkaline because it changes colour at about pH 7. It's <u>red</u> in <u>acidic</u> solutions, <u>purple</u> in <u>neutral</u> solutions and <u>blue</u> in <u>alkaline</u> solutions.

| Acidic | Neutral | Alkaline |

3) <u>Phenolphthalein</u> will change from <u>colourless</u> in <u>acidic</u> solutions to <u>bright pink</u> in <u>alkaline</u> solutions.

Acidic   Alkaline

4) <u>Methyl orange</u> changes from <u>red</u> in <u>acidic</u> solutions to <u>yellow</u> in <u>alkaline</u> solutions.

Acidic Alkaline

Acids can be Neutralised by Bases (or Alkalis)

> An <u>ACID</u> is a source of <u>hydrogen ions</u> (H^+). Acids have a pH of less than 7.
> A <u>BASE</u> is a substance that can neutralise an acid. <u>ALKALIS</u> are <u>soluble bases</u>.
> An alkali is a source of <u>hydroxide ions</u> (OH^-) and has a pH greater than 7.

The reaction between an acid and a base (or an acid and an alkali) is called <u>neutralisation</u>. Make sure you learn it:

$$\text{acid} + \text{base} \rightarrow \text{salt} + \text{water}$$

Neutralisation can also be seen in terms of H^+ and OH^- ions like this, so learn it too:

$$H^+_{(aq)} + OH^-_{(aq)} \rightarrow H_2O_{(l)}$$

When an acid neutralises a base (or vice versa), the <u>products</u> are <u>neutral</u>, i.e. they have a <u>pH of 7</u>.

Interesting(ish) fact — your skin is slightly acidic (pH 5.5)...

The neutralisation reaction's a great one to know. If you have <u>indigestion</u>, it's because you've got too much hydrochloric acid in your stomach. Indigestion tablets contain bases that neutralise the acid.

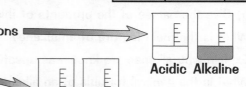

Reactions of Acids

Acids are an enthusiastic bunch — they get involved in loads of reactions. For example, they can react with <u>metals</u> (see page 34), <u>metal oxides</u> and <u>metal carbonates</u>.

Acids <u>react with</u> Metal Oxides <u>to make</u> Salt + Water...

1) <u>Metal oxides</u> are generally <u>bases</u>.
2) This means they'll <u>react with acids</u> to form <u>a salt</u> and <u>water</u>.

$$\boxed{\text{Acid} + \text{Metal Oxide} \rightarrow \text{Salt} + \text{Water}}$$

3) If the acid is <u>hydrochloric acid</u> the salt will be a metal <u>chloride</u>. If it's <u>sulfuric acid</u> the salt will be a metal <u>sulfate</u>. And if it's <u>nitric acid</u> the salt will be a metal <u>nitrate</u>.

For example:

hydrochloric acid + copper oxide → copper chloride + water
$$2HCl \quad + \quad CuO \quad \rightarrow \quad CuCl_2 \quad + \quad H_2O$$

Copper ion is Cu^{2+}, so it needs two Cl^- ions.

sulfuric acid + zinc oxide → zinc sulfate + water
$$H_2SO_4 \quad + \quad ZnO \quad \rightarrow \quad ZnSO_4 \quad + \quad H_2O$$

nitric acid + copper oxide → copper nitrate + water
$$2HNO_3 \quad + \quad CuO \quad \rightarrow \quad Cu(NO_3)_2 \quad + \quad H_2O$$

...and with Metal Carbonates <u>to give</u> Salt + Water + Carbon Dioxide

More gripping reactions involving acids. At least there are some <u>bubbles</u> involved here.

$$\boxed{\text{Acid} + \text{Metal Carbonate} \rightarrow \text{Salt} + \text{Water} + \text{Carbon Dioxide}}$$

As with metal oxides, the <u>type of salt</u> you get out of the reaction depends on the <u>acid</u> you use. Here are some examples:

hydrochloric acid + sodium carbonate → sodium chloride + water + carbon dioxide
$$2HCl + Na_2CO_3 \rightarrow 2NaCl + H_2O + CO_2$$

sulfuric acid + calcium carbonate → calcium sulfate + water + carbon dioxide
$$H_2SO_4 + CaCO_3 \rightarrow CaSO_4 + H_2O + CO_2$$

nitric acid + calcium carbonate → calcium nitrate + water + carbon dioxide
$$2HNO_3 + CaCO_3 \rightarrow Ca(NO_3)_2 + H_2O + CO_2$$

Don't forget to balance your equations.

Kettle + acid → tea + stomach ache...

The acid + carbonate reaction is one you might have to do at home. If you live in a <u>hard water</u> area, you'll get insoluble $MgCO_3$ and $CaCO_3$ 'furring up' your kettle. You can get rid of this with 'descaler', which is dilute <u>acid</u> (often citric acid) — this reacts with the <u>insoluble carbonates</u> to make <u>soluble salts</u>.

Making Salts

Making salts is easy — you just need to know if they're <u>soluble</u> or <u>insoluble</u>...

Salts can be Soluble or Insoluble

Some salts are soluble (dissolve) in water, others are insoluble (won't dissolve):

- <u>Sodium</u>, <u>potassium</u> and <u>ammonium</u> salts are <u>soluble</u>.
- <u>Nitrates</u> are <u>soluble</u>.
- Most <u>chlorides</u> are <u>soluble</u> — except for silver chloride.
- Most <u>sulfates</u> are <u>soluble</u> — except barium sulfate and calcium sulfate.
- Most <u>carbonates</u> are <u>insoluble</u> — except sodium, potassium and ammonium carbonates.

Making Soluble Salts Using Acids and Insoluble Bases

1) You need to pick the right <u>acid</u>, plus an <u>insoluble base</u> (most <u>metal oxides</u>, <u>metal carbonates</u> and <u>metal hydroxides</u> are insoluble). E.g. if you want to make <u>copper nitrate</u>, mix <u>nitric acid</u> and <u>copper carbonate</u>.

$$CuCO_{3 (s)} + 2HNO_{3 (aq)} \longrightarrow Cu(NO_3)_{2 (aq)} + CO_{2 (g)} + H_2O_{(l)}$$

2) You add the <u>metal oxide</u>, <u>carbonate</u> or <u>hydroxide</u> to the <u>acid</u> — the solid will <u>dissolve</u> in the acid as it reacts. You'll know when all the acid has been neutralised because the excess solid will <u>sink</u> to the bottom of the flask and remain there.

3) You can then <u>filter</u> out the <u>excess</u> base to get the <u>salt solution</u>. To get <u>pure</u>, <u>solid</u> crystals of the <u>salt</u>, <u>evaporate</u> off the water.

filter paper
filter funnel

Making Soluble Salts Using an Alkali

1) You can't use the method above if you want to neutralise an <u>acid</u> with an <u>alkali</u>. Alkalis are <u>soluble</u> bases so you <u>can't filter them out</u> if you add <u>too much</u> — in fact you can't tell when you've added too much.

2) You have to add <u>exactly</u> the right amount of alkali to <u>just neutralise</u> the acid — you need to use an <u>indicator</u> (see page 50) to show when the reaction's finished. The best way of doing this is to do a <u>titration</u> — see next page. Then <u>repeat</u> using exactly the same volumes of alkali and acid but <u>without an indicator</u> so the salt isn't <u>contaminated</u>.

Making Insoluble Salts — Precipitation Reactions

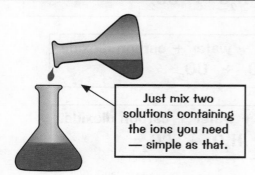

Just mix two solutions containing the ions you need — simple as that.

1) If the salt you want to make is <u>insoluble</u>, you can use a <u>precipitation reaction</u>.

2) You just need to pick <u>two solutions</u> that contain the <u>ions</u> you need. E.g. to make <u>barium sulfate</u> (which is insoluble) you need a solution which contains <u>barium ions</u> and one which contains <u>sulfate ions</u>. So you can mix <u>barium chloride</u> (most chlorides are soluble) with <u>sulfuric acid</u>.

E.g. $$BaCl_{2 (aq)} + H_2SO_{4 (aq)} \longrightarrow BaSO_{4 (s)} + 2HCl_{(aq)}$$

Get two beakers, mix 'em together — job's a good 'un...

Well, maybe it's not quite that simple — you do need to learn the details too I'm afraid. And make sure you learn which salts are soluble and which aren't so you know what you're filtering out (the <u>salt</u> or the <u>base</u>). Once you've done that you can move on to titrations. There's no filtering involved there, as you'll see on the next page...

Titrations

Titrations have a bad reputation — but they're not as bad as they're made out to be.

Titrations **are Used to Find Out** Concentrations

You can also do titrations the other way round — adding alkali to acid.

1) Titrations allow you to find out exactly how much acid is needed to neutralise a quantity of alkali (or vice versa). Here's how you do a titration...

2) Using a pipette and pipette filler, add some alkali (usually about 25 cm³) to a conical flask, along with two or three drops of indicator. (The pipette filler stops you getting a mouthful of alkali.)

3) Fill a burette with the acid. Make sure you do this BELOW EYE LEVEL — you don't want to be looking up if some acid spills over.

4) Using the burette, add the acid to the alkali a bit at a time — giving the conical flask a regular swirl. Go especially slowly when you think the end-point (colour change) is about to be reached.

5) The indicator changes colour when all the alkali has been neutralised, e.g. phenolphthalein is pink in alkalis, but colourless in acids.

6) Record the volume of acid used to neutralise the alkali. It's best to repeat this process a few times, making sure you get (pretty much) the same answer each time — this makes for more reliable results.

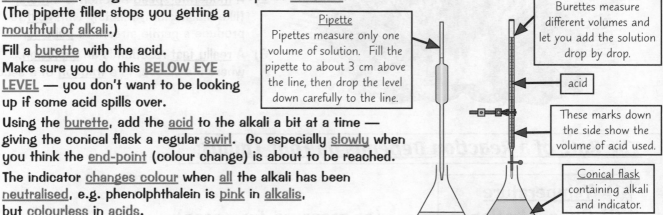

Pipette
Pipettes measure only one volume of solution. Fill the pipette to about 3 cm above the line, then drop the level down carefully to the line.

Burette
Burettes measure different volumes and let you add the solution drop by drop.

acid

These marks down the side show the volume of acid used.

Conical flask containing alkali and indicator.

The Calculation — **Work Out the** Numbers of Moles

Now for the calculations... basically, you're trying to find the number of moles of each substance (see p. 21). A formula triangle is pretty handy here, I reckon. (And it's the same one as on page 24, conveniently.)

Example: Suppose you start off with 25 cm³ of sodium hydroxide solution in your flask, and you know that its concentration is 0.1 moles per dm³.

You then find from your titration that it takes 30 cm³ of sulfuric acid (of an unknown concentration) to neutralise the sodium hydroxide.

Find the concentration of the acid.

Step 1: Work out how many moles of the 'known' substance you have:

Number of moles = concentration × volume = 0.1 × (25 / 1000) = 0.0025 moles

Step 2: Write down the equation for the reaction...

$2NaOH + H_2SO_4 \longrightarrow Na_2SO_4 + 2H_2O$

...and work out how many moles of the 'unknown' stuff you must have had.

Using the equation, you can see that for every two moles of sodium hydroxide you had...
...there was just one mole of sulfuric acid.

So if you had 0.0025 moles of sodium hydroxide...
...you must have had 0.0025 ÷ 2 = 0.00125 moles of sulfuric acid.

Step 3: Work out the concentration of the 'unknown' stuff.

Concentration = number of moles ÷ volume
= 0.00125 ÷ (30 / 1000) = 0.0417 moles per dm³

If you need the concentration in g/dm³, convert your answer using the method on page 24.

If you can spell phenolphthalein — you deserve a chemistry qualification...

The indicator's job is to tell you when the reaction is finished. Phenolphthalein is good for acids and alkalis, but other indicators are possible too. However, don't use universal indicator — it's too hard to tell accurately when the reaction is over. You want an indicator that gives a sudden colour change.

Rates of Reaction

Reactions Can Go at All Sorts of Different Rates

1) One of the <u>slowest</u> is the <u>rusting</u> of iron (it's not slow enough though — what about my poor little car).

2) A <u>moderate speed</u> reaction is a <u>metal</u> (like magnesium) reacting with <u>acid</u> to produce a gentle stream of <u>bubbles</u>.

3) A <u>really fast</u> reaction is an <u>explosion</u>, where it's all over in a <u>fraction</u> of a second.

The Rate of a Reaction Depends on Four Things:

1) <u>Temperature</u>
2) <u>Concentration</u>   — (or <u>pressure</u> for gases)
3) <u>Catalyst</u>
4) <u>Size of particles</u>   — (or <u>surface area</u>)

LEARN THEM!

Typical Graphs for Rate of Reaction

The plot below shows how the speed of a particular reaction varies under <u>different conditions</u>. The quickest reaction is shown by the line that becomes <u>flat</u> in the <u>least</u> time. The line that flattens out first must have the <u>steepest slope</u> compared to all the others, making it possible to spot the slowest and fastest reactions.

1) <u>Graph 1</u> represents the original <u>fairly slow</u> reaction. The graph is not too steep.

2) <u>Graphs 2 and 3</u> represent the reaction taking place <u>quicker</u> but with the <u>same initial amounts</u>. The slope of the graphs gets steeper.

3) The <u>increased rate</u> could be due to <u>any</u> of these:

> 1) increase in <u>temperature</u>
> 2) increase in <u>concentration</u> (or pressure)
> 3) <u>catalyst</u> added
> 4) solid reactant crushed up into <u>smaller bits</u> (so it has a bigger surface area).

Amount of product evolved

④ faster, and more reactants

End of Reaction

③ much faster reaction

② faster reaction

① original reaction

Time

4) <u>Graph 4</u> produces <u>more product</u> as well as going <u>faster</u>. This can <u>only</u> happen if <u>more reactant(s)</u> are added at the start. <u>Graphs 1, 2 and 3</u> all converge at the same level, showing that they all produce the same amount of product, although they take <u>different</u> times to get there.

How to get a fast, furious reaction — crack a wee joke...

<u>Industrial</u> reactions generally use a <u>catalyst</u> and are done at <u>high temperature and pressure</u>. Time is money, so the faster an industrial reaction goes the better... but only <u>up to a point</u>. Chemical plants are quite expensive to rebuild if they get blown into lots and lots of teeny tiny pieces.

Measuring Rates of Reaction

Three Ways to Measure the Speed of a Reaction

The speed of a reaction can be observed either by how quickly the reactants are used up or how quickly the products are formed. It's usually a lot easier to measure products forming.

The rate of reaction can be calculated using the following equation:

$$\text{Rate of Reaction} = \frac{\text{Amount of reactant used or amount of product formed}}{\text{Time}}$$

There are different ways that the speed of a reaction can be measured. Learn these three:

1) Precipitation

1) This is when the product of the reaction is a precipitate which clouds the solution.

2) Observe a marker through the solution and measure how long it takes for it to disappear.

3) The quicker the marker disappears, the quicker the reaction.

4) This only works for reactions where the initial solution is rather see-through.

5) The result is very subjective — different people might not agree over the exact point when the mark 'disappears'.

2) Change in Mass (Usually Gas Given Off)

1) Measuring the speed of a reaction that produces a gas can be carried out on a mass balance.

2) As the gas is released the mass disappearing is easily measured on the balance.

3) The quicker the reading on the balance drops, the faster the reaction.

4) When the mass stops changing, the reaction has finished.

5) Rate of reaction graphs are particularly easy to plot using the results from this method.

6) This is the most accurate of the three methods described on this page because the mass balance is very accurate. But it has the disadvantage of releasing the gas straight into the room.

3) The Volume of Gas Given Off

1) This involves the use of a gas syringe to measure the volume of gas given off.

2) The more gas given off during a given time interval, the faster the reaction.

3) When gas stops being produced, the reaction has finished.

4) A graph of gas volume against time elapsed could be plotted to give a rate of reaction graph.

5) Gas syringes usually give volumes accurate to the nearest millilitre, so they're quite accurate. You have to be quite careful though — if the reaction is too vigorous, you can easily blow the plunger out of the end of the syringe.

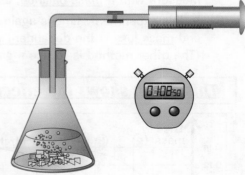

OK have you got your stopwatch ready *BANG!* — oh...

Each method has its pros and cons. The mass balance method is only accurate as long as the flask isn't too hot, otherwise you lose mass by evaporation as well as by the reaction. The first method isn't very accurate, but if you're not producing a gas you can't use either of the other two. Ah well.

Rate of Reaction Experiments

Remember: Any reaction can be used to investigate any of the four factors that affect the rate. These pages illustrate four important reactions, but only one factor has been considered for each. But we could just as easily use, say, the marble chips/acid reaction to test the effect of temperature instead.

1) Reaction of Hydrochloric Acid and Marble Chips

This experiment is often used to demonstrate the effect of breaking the solid up into small bits.

1) Measure the volume of gas evolved with a gas syringe and take readings at regular intervals.

2) Make a table of readings and plot them as a graph. You choose regular time intervals, so time is the independent variable (x) and volume is the dependent variable (y).

3) Repeat the experiment with exactly the same volume of acid, and exactly the same mass of marble chips, but with the marble more crunched up.

4) Then repeat with the same mass of powdered marble instead of marble chips.

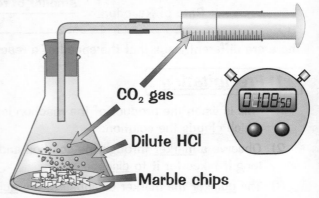

CO₂ gas

Dilute HCl

Marble chips

This graph shows the effect of using finer particles of solid

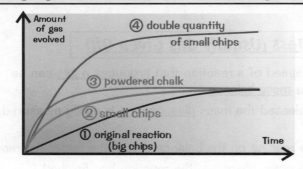

1) An increase in surface area causes more frequent collisions, so the rate of reaction is faster.

2) Line 4 shows the reaction if a greater mass of small marble chips is added.

3) The extra surface area gives a quicker reaction and there is also more gas evolved overall (as long as the acid is in excess).

2) Reaction of Magnesium Metal with Dilute HCl

1) This reaction is good for measuring the effects of increased concentration (as is the marble/acid reaction).

2) This reaction gives off hydrogen gas, which we can measure with a mass balance, as shown.

3) In this experiment, time is again the independent variable and mass loss is the dependent variable. (The other method is to use a gas syringe, as above.)

This graph shows the effect of using more concentrated acid solutions

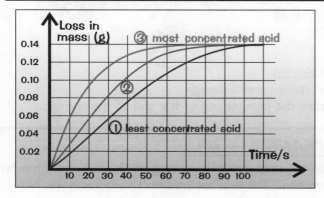

1) Take readings of mass at regular time intervals.

2) Put the results in a table and work out the loss in mass for each reading. Plot a graph.

3) Repeat with more concentrated acid solutions, but always with the same amount of magnesium.

4) The volume of acid must always be kept the same too — only the concentration is increased.

5) The three graphs show the same old pattern — a higher concentration giving a steeper graph, with the reaction finishing much quicker.

Rate of Reaction Experiments

3) Sodium Thiosulfate and HCl Produce a Cloudy Precipitate

1) These two chemicals are both <u>clear solutions</u>.

2) They react together to form a <u>yellow precipitate</u> of <u>sulfur</u>.

3) The experiment involves watching a black mark <u>disappear</u> through the <u>cloudy sulfur</u> and <u>timing</u> how long it takes to go.

4) The reaction can be <u>repeated</u> for solutions at different <u>temperatures</u>. In practice, that's quite hard to do accurately and safely (it's not a good idea to heat an acid directly). The best way to do it is to use a <u>water bath</u> to heat both solutions to the right temperature <u>before you mix them</u>.

5) The <u>depth</u> of liquid must be kept the <u>same</u> each time, of course.

6) The results will of course show that the <u>higher</u> the temperature the <u>quicker</u> the reaction and therefore the <u>less time</u> it takes for the mark to <u>disappear</u>. These are typical results:

	Temperature (°C)	20	25	30	35	40
independent variable →						
dependent variable →	Time taken for mark to disappear (s)	193	151	112	87	52

This reaction can <u>also</u> be used to test the effects of <u>concentration</u>.

One sad thing about this reaction is it <u>doesn't</u> give a set of graphs. Well I think it's sad. All you get is a set of <u>readings</u> of how long it took till the mark disappeared for each temperature. Boring.

4) The Decomposition of Hydrogen Peroxide

This is a <u>good</u> reaction for showing the effect of different <u>catalysts</u>.

The decomposition of hydrogen peroxide is:

$$2H_2O_{2\,(aq)} \rightarrow 2H_2O_{(l)} + O_{2\,(g)}$$

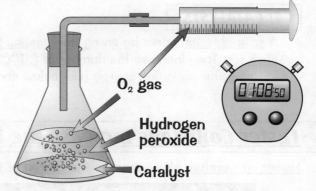

1) This is normally quite <u>slow</u> but a sprinkle of <u>manganese(IV) oxide catalyst</u> speeds it up no end. Other catalysts which work are found in: a) <u>potato peel</u> and b) <u>blood</u>.

2) <u>Oxygen gas</u> is given off, which provides an <u>ideal way</u> to measure the rate of reaction using the good ol' <u>gas syringe</u> method.

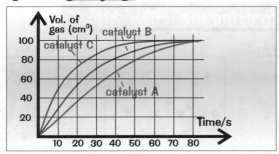

3) Same old graphs of course.

4) <u>Better</u> catalysts give a <u>quicker reaction</u>, which is shown by a <u>steeper graph</u> which levels off quickly.

5) This reaction can also be used to measure the effects of <u>temperature</u>, or of <u>concentration</u> of the H_2O_2 solution. The graphs will look just the same.

BLOOD is a catalyst? — eeurgh...

You don't need to know all the details of these specific reactions — it's the <u>experimental methods</u> you need to learn. If you understand how all this works, you should be able to apply it to any reaction.

Collision Theory

Reaction rates are explained perfectly by collision theory. It's really simple.

It just says that the rate of a reaction simply depends on how often and how hard the reacting particles collide with each other. The basic idea is that particles have to collide in order to react, and they have to collide hard enough (with enough energy).

More Collisions Increases the Rate of Reaction

All four methods of increasing the rate of reactions can be explained in terms of increasing the number of successful collisions per second between the reacting particles:

1) HIGHER TEMPERATURE

When the temperature is increased the particles have more energy and move quicker. If they're moving quicker, they're going to collide more frequently.

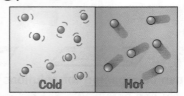

2) HIGHER CONCENTRATION (or PRESSURE)

If a solution is made more concentrated it means there are more particles of reactant knocking about between the water molecules which makes collisions between the important particles more likely. In a gas, increasing the pressure means the particles are more squashed up together so they are going to collide more frequently.

As a reaction progresses there are fewer and fewer reactant particles, so they collide less frequently and the reaction rate slows down.

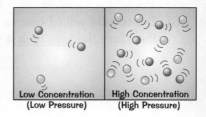

3) LARGER SURFACE AREA

If one of the reactants is a solid then breaking it up into smaller pieces will increase its surface area. This means the particles around it in the solution will have more area to work on, so there'll be useful collisions more often.

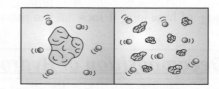

4) CATALYSTS

A solid catalyst works by giving the reacting particles a surface to stick to. They increase the number of SUCCESSFUL collisions by lowering the activation energy (see below and page 60).

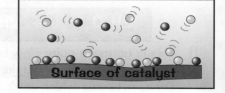

Faster Collisions Increase the Rate of Reaction

Higher temperature also increases the energy of the collisions, because it makes all the particles move faster.

Faster collisions are ONLY caused by increasing the temperature

Reactions only happen if the particles collide with enough energy.

At a higher temperature there will be more particles colliding with enough energy to make the reaction happen — we say there are more successful collisions.

This initial energy is known as the activation energy and it's needed to break the initial bonds.

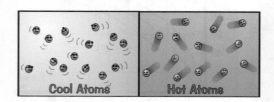

Collision theory — the lamppost ran into me...

Once you've learnt everything on this page, the rates of reaction stuff should start making a lot more sense.
To sum up — the more often and harder particles bump into each other, the faster the reaction happens.

Energy Transfer in Reactions

In a chemical reaction, <u>energy</u> can be <u>transferred</u> to or from the <u>surroundings</u>, and it's all about making and breaking bonds.

Energy Must Always be <u>Supplied</u> to <u>Break Bonds</u>

1) During a chemical reaction, <u>old bonds are broken</u> and <u>new bonds are formed</u>.

2) Energy must be <u>supplied</u> to break <u>existing bonds</u> — so bond breaking is an <u>endothermic</u> process.

3) Energy is <u>released</u> when new bonds are <u>formed</u> — so bond formation is an <u>exothermic</u> process.

In an <u>Exothermic</u> Reaction, Energy is <u>Given Out</u>

In an <u>EXOTHERMIC</u> reaction, the energy <u>released</u> in bond formation is <u>greater</u> than the energy used in <u>breaking</u> old bonds.

> An <u>EXOTHERMIC</u> <u>reaction</u> is one which <u>GIVES OUT ENERGY</u> to the surroundings, usually in the form of <u>heat</u> and usually shown by a <u>RISE IN TEMPERATURE</u>.

In an <u>Endothermic</u> Reaction, Energy is <u>Taken In</u>

In an <u>ENDOTHERMIC</u> reaction, the energy <u>required</u> to break old bonds is <u>greater</u> than the energy <u>released</u> when <u>new bonds</u> are formed.

> An <u>ENDOTHERMIC</u> <u>reaction</u> is one which <u>TAKES IN ENERGY</u> from the surroundings, usually in the form of <u>heat</u> and usually shown by a <u>FALL IN TEMPERATURE</u>.

The <u>Change in Energy</u> is Called the <u>Enthalpy Change</u>

> The <u>overall change</u> in energy in a reaction is called the <u>ENTHALPY</u> change. It has the symbol $\triangle H$.

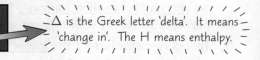
$\triangle$ is the Greek letter 'delta'. It means 'change in'. The H means enthalpy.

1) The units of $\triangle H$ are <u>kJ/mol</u> — so it's the amount of energy in kilojoules per mole of reactant.

2) Enthalpy change can have a <u>positive</u> value or a <u>negative</u> value.
   - If the reaction is <u>exothermic</u>, the value is <u>negative</u> because the reaction is <u>giving out</u> energy.
   - If the reaction is <u>endothermic</u>, the value is <u>positive</u> because the reaction <u>takes in</u> energy.

<u>Right, so burning gives out heat — really...</u>

This whole energy transfer thing is a fairly simple idea — don't be put off by the long words.
Remember, "<u>exo-</u>" = <u>exit</u>, "<u>-thermic</u>" = <u>heat</u>, so an exothermic reaction is one that <u>gives out</u> heat.
And "<u>endo-</u>" = erm... the other one. Okay, so there's no easy way to remember that one. Tough.

Energy Level Diagrams

Energy level diagrams show how the energy levels of the reactants change when they react to form the products.

Energy Level Diagrams Show if it's Exo- or Endo-thermic

In exothermic reactions   ΔH is –ve ← ΔH is the enthalpy change (see page 59).

1) This shows an exothermic reaction — the products are at a lower energy than the reactants.

2) The difference in height represents the energy given out in the reaction (per mole). ΔH is –ve here.

3) The initial rise in the line represents the energy needed to break the old bonds. This is the activation energy.

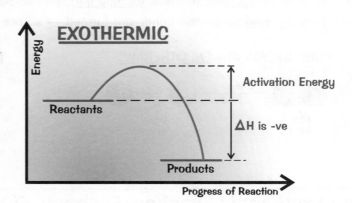

In endothermic reactions   ΔH is +ve

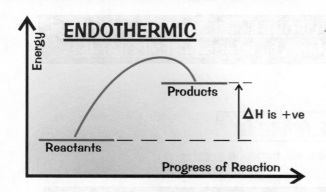

1) This shows an endothermic reaction because the products are at a higher energy than the reactants, so ΔH is +ve.

2) The difference in height represents the energy taken in during the reaction.

The Activation Energy is Lowered by Catalysts

1) The activation energy represents the minimum energy needed by reacting particles for the reaction to occur.

2) A catalyst makes reactions happen faster by providing an alternative reaction pathway (i.e another way for the particles to react) with a lower activation energy.

3) This is represented by the lower curve on the diagram, which shows that less initial energy is needed for the reaction to begin.

4) The overall energy change for the reaction, ΔH, remains the same though.

Catalysts are not used up during reactions.

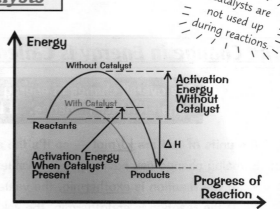

Energy transfer — make sure you take it all in...

So for exothermic reactions, there's a step down on the energy level diagram 'cause the products have less energy than the reactants. In endothermic reactions, it's the other way round — there's a step up from reactants to products. And catalysts handily reduce the activation energy needed to kick off a reaction. Sorted.

Bond Energy Calculations

You can <u>calculate</u> the <u>enthalpy change</u> for a reaction by looking at the bonds that are made and broken.

Bond Energy — The Amount of Energy in a Bond

1) <u>Each type</u> of chemical bond (e.g. C–C or C–H) has a particular <u>bond energy</u> associated with it.
2) This <u>bond energy</u> can vary slightly depending what <u>compound</u> the bond is in — so you'll be given <u>average bond energies</u> in the exam.
3) You can use these to calculate the <u>enthalpy</u> change for a reaction. The basic idea is really simple — <u>add up</u> the energy of the bonds that are <u>broken</u> and <u>subtract</u> the energy of the bonds that are <u>made</u>.

Example: The Formation of HCl

Using bond energies you can <u>calculate</u> the <u>enthalpy change</u> for this reaction:

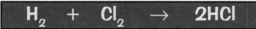

$$H_2 \ + \ Cl_2 \ \rightarrow \ 2HCl$$

The bond energies you need are:

H–H: +436 kJ/mol
Cl–Cl: +242 kJ/mol
H–Cl: +431 kJ/mol

1) <u>BREAKING one mole</u> of H–H and one mole of Cl–Cl bonds <u>requires</u>:
   436 + 242 = <u>678 kJ</u>

2) <u>FORMING two moles</u> of H–Cl bonds <u>releases</u>:
   2 × 431 = <u>862 kJ</u>

3) Then use this formula to calculate the difference:

Enthalpy change ($\triangle H$) =	Total energy absorbed to break bonds	—	Total energy released in making bonds

4) So, $\triangle H$ = 678 – 862 = <u>–184 kJ/mol</u>
5) The $\triangle H$ is <u>negative</u>, so the reaction must be <u>exothermic</u>.

You can even draw all this out on an <u>energy level diagram</u>:

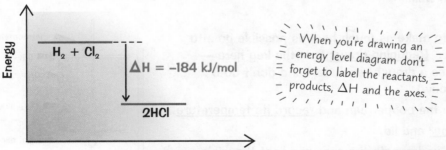

When you're drawing an energy level diagram don't forget to label the reactants, products, $\triangle H$ and the axes.

You might get given a slightly <u>more complicated</u> reaction where there are more bonds to break and make, but the method is <u>just the same</u>.

For example in the reaction:
$$CH_4 + 2O_2 \rightarrow CO_2 + 2H_2O$$
There are <u>4 × C–H</u> bonds broken, <u>2 × O=O</u> bonds broken, <u>2 × C=O</u> bonds made and <u>4 × O–H</u> bonds made.

"The name's Bond, C–H Bond..." — sorry, I couldn't help it...

These calculations might look scary but really they're quite straightforward. Whatever the reaction is, the method is <u>always the same</u> — calculate the energy of <u>all the bonds that are broken</u> and the energy of <u>all the bonds that are made</u>, then plug them in the <u>formula</u>. Voilà. Then sit back and be proud you've mastered enthalpy change.

Paper 2

Paper 2

Paper 2

Measuring Enthalpy Changes

Did you know that you can actually <u>measure</u> all this enthalpy stuff in the lab... oh yes, read on...

You can find out Enthalpy Changes using Calorimetry

<u>Calorimetry</u> allows you to measure the amount of <u>energy transferred</u> in a <u>chemical reaction</u> with a pretty simple set of equipment. Here are two different types of experiment you can do:

Calorimetry — Dissolving, Displacement and Neutralisation Reactions

To measure the amount of <u>energy transferred</u> in these <u>reactions</u> (in solution) you just take the <u>temperature of the reagents</u> (making sure they're the same), <u>mix</u> them and measure the <u>temperature of the solution</u> at the <u>end</u> of the reaction. Easy.

1) So if you want to investigate the enthalpy change of <u>dissolving</u>, <u>displacement</u> (see page 33) or <u>neutralisation</u> reactions (see page 50) you can do it by mixing the reactants in a <u>polystyrene cup</u> (very technical).

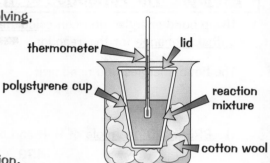

2) The biggest <u>problem</u> with energy measurements is the amount of energy <u>lost to the surroundings</u>.

3) You can reduce it a bit by putting the polystyrene cup into a <u>beaker of cotton wool</u> to give <u>more insulation</u>, and putting a <u>lid</u> on the cup to reduce energy lost by <u>evaporation</u>.

> Example:
> 1) Place 25 cm³ of dilute hydrochloric acid in a polystyrene cup, and record the temperature of the acid.
> 2) Put 25 cm³ of dilute sodium hydroxide solution in a measuring cylinder and record its temperature.
> 3) Add the alkali to the acid and stir.
> 4) Take the temperature of the mixture every 30 seconds, and record the highest temperature it reaches.

Calorimetry — Combustion

To measure the amount of energy produced when a fuel is burnt, you can simply burn the fuel and use the flame to <u>heat up some water</u>. This method uses a <u>metal container</u>, usually made of <u>copper</u> because copper conducts heat so well.
Method:

1) It's dead important to make as much heat as possible go into <u>heating up</u> the water. <u>Reducing draughts</u> is the key here — use a <u>screen</u> to act as a draught excluder (and don't do it next to an open window).

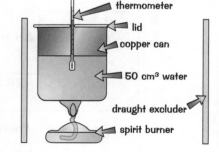

2) Put 50 g of water in the copper can and <u>record its temperature</u>.

3) <u>Weigh the spirit burner</u> and lid.

4) Put the spirit burner underneath the can, and light the wick. Heat the water, <u>stirring constantly</u>, until the temperature reaches about <u>50 °C</u>.

5) <u>Put out the flame</u> using the burner lid, and measure the <u>final temperature</u> of the water.

6) <u>Weigh</u> the spirit burner and lid <u>again</u>.

7) You can then use the measurements you've taken to <u>calculate the enthalpy change</u> — see the next page.

I like my experiments how I like my coffee — in a polystyrene cup...

Just the two <u>experimental methods</u> to learn from this page. Make sure you know which set-up you would use for which <u>type of reaction</u>, and how to <u>stop energy being lost</u> to the surroundings. I think you know the way to do it. Cover the page and write it all out — keep going till you can remember every last bit.

Calculating Enthalpy Changes

If you've read the previous page, you'll know how to get temperature measurements from the start and end of reactions and to work out how much fuel was used for combustion. Now it's calculations time... woo...

Calculate the Heat Energy Transferred

1) The combustion experiment on the previous page involves heating water by burning a liquid fuel.

2) If you measure (i) how much fuel you've burned and (ii) the temperature change of the water, you can work out how much energy is supplied by each gram of fuel.

3) You also need to know water's specific heat capacity — this is the amount of energy needed to raise the temperature of 1 gram of water by 1 °C. The specific heat capacity of water is 4.2 J/g/°C — so it takes 4.2 joules of energy to raise the temperature of 1 g of water by 1 °C.

Example: to work out the energy per gram of methylated spirit (meths):

Mass of spirit burner + lid before heating = 68.75 g
Mass of spirit burner + lid after heating = 67.85 g
→ Mass of meths burnt = 0.90 g

Temperature of water in copper can before heating = 21.5 °C
Temperature of water in copper can after heating = 52.5 °C
→ Temperature rise of 50 g of water due to heating = 31.0 °C

So 0.90 g of fuel produces enough energy to heat up 50 g of water by 31 °C.
It takes 4.2 joules of energy to heat up 1 g of water by 1 °C. You'll be told this in the exam.
Therefore, the energy produced in this experiment = 4.2 × 50 × 31 = 6510 joules.

So 0.9 g of meths produces 6510 joules of energy...
...meaning 1 g of meths produces 6510/0.9 = 7233 J or 7.233 kJ

Energy's wasted heating the can, air, etc. So this figure will often be much lower than the actual energy content.

Calculate the Molar Enthalpy Change

Once you've calculated the amount of energy produced you can use it to work out the molar enthalpy change (the enthalpy change given out by one mole of the reactant). See page 21 for more on moles. You need the same info as before and the M_r of the fuel (see page 18).

Example: to work out the energy per mole of methylated spirit (meths):

1 First, calculate the amount of energy transferred.
From the calculation above, we know the energy produced in this experiment = 6510 J or 6.510 kJ

2 Next, you need to find out how many moles of fuel produced this heat. The M_r of meths is 44.6.
It's back to the old number of moles = $\frac{mass (g)}{M_r}$ equation. So, number of moles = $\frac{0.90}{44.6}$ = 0.020 moles

3 So, the heat produced by 1 mole of fuel = $\frac{-6.510}{0.020}$ ≈ -325.5 kJ/mol
The sign has changed to negative because combustion is an exothermic reaction.

Get this right in the exam and you might be as happy as this cowboy.

AHHHHHHHHHHHHH — calculations...

But they're not that bad once you get your head around them — once you've remembered the steps all you have to do is remember your formulas. Don't worry, take a deep breath and have a read over this page a few times.

Reversible Reactions

A <u>reversible reaction</u> is one where the <u>products</u> of the reaction can react with each other and <u>convert back</u> to the original reactants. In other words, <u>it can go both ways</u>.

> A <u>reversible reaction</u> is one where the <u>products</u> of the
> reaction can <u>themselves react</u> to produce the <u>original reactants</u>.
>
> A + B $\rightleftharpoons$ C + D

This is the symbol for a reversible reaction.

The <u>thermal decomposition of ammonium chloride</u> is a reversible reaction.

1) Ammonium chloride is a <u>white solid</u>. When it's heated it breaks down into the gases <u>ammonia</u> and <u>hydrogen chloride</u> — this is the <u>forward reaction</u>.

$$NH_4Cl_{(s)} \rightleftharpoons NH_{3(g)} + HCl_{(g)}$$

2) If you let it cool the <u>ammonia</u> and <u>hydrogen chloride</u> react to <u>re-form</u> the solid — this is the <u>backward reaction</u>.

The <u>dehydration of copper(II) sulfate</u> is another example of a reversible reaction (see page 43).

Reversible Reactions Will Reach *Dynamic Equilibrium*

1) If a reversible reaction takes place in a <u>closed system</u> then a state of <u>equilibrium</u> will always be reached.

2) <u>Equilibrium</u> means that the <u>relative (%) quantities</u> of reactants and products will reach a certain <u>balance</u> and stay there. (A '<u>closed system</u>' just means that none of the reactants or products can <u>escape</u>.)

3) It is in fact a <u>DYNAMIC EQUILIBRIUM</u>, which means that the reactions are still taking place in <u>both directions</u>, but the <u>overall effect is nil</u> because the forward and reverse reactions <u>cancel</u> each other out. The reactions are taking place at <u>exactly the same rate</u> in both directions.

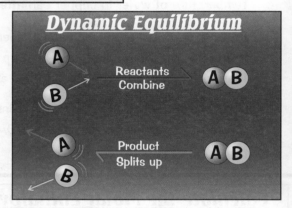

Dynamic Equilibrium

Changing *Temperature* and *Pressure* Can Get You *More Product*

1) In a reversible reaction the '<u>position of equilibrium</u>' (the relative amounts of reactants and products) depends <u>very strongly</u> on the <u>temperature</u> and <u>pressure</u> of the reacting mixture.

2) If you <u>deliberately alter</u> the temperature and pressure you can <u>move</u> the "position of equilibrium" to give <u>more product</u> and <u>less</u> reactants.

TEMPERATURE

All reactions are <u>exothermic</u> in one direction and <u>endothermic</u> in the other.
- If you <u>raise</u> the <u>temperature</u>, the <u>endothermic</u> reaction will increase to <u>use up</u> the extra heat.
- If you <u>reduce</u> the <u>temperature</u>, the <u>exothermic</u> reaction will increase to <u>give out</u> more heat.

PRESSURE

Most gaseous reactions have <u>more molecules</u> (or <u>moles</u>) of gas on one side than on the other.
- If you <u>raise</u> the <u>pressure</u> it will encourage the reaction which produces <u>fewer molecules</u> of gas.
- If you <u>lower</u> the <u>pressure</u> it will encourage the reaction which produces <u>more molecules</u> of gas.

Beep beep beep — this reaction is reversing...

Changing the temperature <u>always</u> changes the equilibrium position, but that's not true of pressure. If your reaction has the same number of molecules on each side of the equation, changing the pressure won't make any difference at all to the equilibrium position (it still affects the <u>rate</u> of reaction though).

Revision Summary for Section 4

This section is a toughie. With all the different colours, reactions, methods and calculations there sure is a lot to remember. If you're feeling overwhelmed by it all, don't be. I've prepared a little something that will help ease you through it. So, find your favourite chair, put on your most comfortable revision pants, kick back and relax — here come the revision summary questions.

1) What range does the pH scale go from and to? What value is given to a neutral solution?

2) What colour does litmus paper go in: a) acidic solutions b) alkaline solutions?

3) Write out the word equation for the reaction between an acid and a base.

4)* Write out the chemical equation for the reaction between hydrochloric acid and zinc carbonate.

5) Are potassium salts soluble or insoluble?

6) Is silver chloride soluble or insoluble?

7) Name three different pieces of equipment you'd need to carry out a titration and say what you'd use each one for.

8)* Suppose you start off with 25 cm³ of sodium hydroxide solution in a conical flask and its concentration is 0.25 moles per dm³. You find from your titration that it takes 42 cm³ of hydrochloric acid to neutralise the sodium hydroxide. What is the concentration of the acid?

9) Name four things that the rate of a reaction depends on.

10) Describe three different methods of measuring the rate of a reaction. Give one advantage and one disadvantage of each method.

11) A student carries out an experiment to measure the effect of surface area on the reaction between marble chips and hydrochloric acid. He measures the amount of gas given off at regular intervals.
    a) Give two factors he must keep constant for it to be a fair test.
    b)* He uses four samples for his experiment:
        Sample A – 10 g of powdered marble,   Sample B – 10 g of small marble chips,
        Sample C – 10 g of large marble chips,   Sample D – 5 g of powdered marble.
        Sketch a graph to show how the amount of gas collected for each sample would change throughout the experiment.

12) Explain how each of the four factors that affect reaction rates increases the number of successful collisions between particles.

13) What is an endothermic reaction?

14) What is the symbol for change in enthalpy?

15) Draw an energy level diagram for an exothermic reaction.

16) What does a catalyst do to the activation energy of a reaction? Show this on your energy level diagram.

17) a)* Calculate the energy change for the following reaction: $2H_2 + O_2 \rightarrow 2H_2O$
        You need these bond energies: H–H: +436 kJ/mol, O=O: +496 kJ/mol, O–H: +463 kJ/mol
        Hint: There are 2 O–H bonds in each molecule of water.
    b)* Is this an exothermic or endothermic reaction?

18) The apparatus below is used to measure how much energy is released when pentane is burnt. It takes 4.2 joules of energy to heat 1 g of water by 1 °C.

    a)* Using the following data, calculate the amount of energy per gram of pentane.

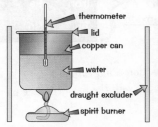

| Mass of empty copper can | 64 g | | Initial temperature of water | 17 °C |
| Mass of copper can + water | 116 g | | Final temperature of water | 47 °C |

| Mass of spirt burner + pentane before burning | 97.72 g |
| Mass of spirt burner + pentane after burning | 97.37 g |

    b) A data book says that pentane has 49 kJ/g of energy. Why is the amount you calculated different?

19) What is a reversible reaction? Explain what is meant by a dynamic equilibrium.

20) How does changing the temperature and pressure of a reversible reaction alter the equilibrium position?

*Answers on page 84.

Section 4 — Physical Chemistry

Metal Ores

Chemistry in industry — time to find out how all those abstract chemical concepts are used in real life. Betcha can't wait. First up — how to get hold of metals. Most metals can't be found as pure lumps. You have to extract them from a compound. And how do you do that, I hear you cry... Funny you should ask...

Most Metals are Found in Ores

1) Metals that are unreactive don't tend to form compounds with other elements. Unreactive metals such as gold are found uncombined — so you just have to find them and dig 'em up.

2) However, most metals do react with other elements to form compounds, which can be found naturally in the Earth's crust. If a compound contains enough of the metal to make it worthwhile extracting, the compound is called a metal ore. There are limited amounts of metal ores — they're "finite resources".

3) The more reactive a metal is, the harder it is to extract it from a compound.

Metals Often have to be Separated from their Oxides

1) Lots of common metals, like iron and aluminium, react with oxygen to form oxides. These oxides are often the ores that the metals need to be extracted from.

2) A reaction that separates a metal from the oxygen in its oxide is called a reduction reaction.

> **REDUCTION — LOSS OF OXYGEN**
>
> E.g. copper oxide is reduced to copper.
>
> $$2CuO + C \longrightarrow 2Cu + CO_2$$

3) In a reduction reaction, the substance that reduces the metal (and is oxidised) is called the reducing agent.

4) The most common type of reduction reaction uses carbon as a reducing agent to separate the oxygen from the metal.

5) But carbon can't be used for all metals...

Methods of Extraction are Linked to the Order of Reactivity

1) Only metals that are less reactive than carbon can be extracted by a reduction reaction with carbon — this is done by heating the ore with carbon monoxide.

2) This is because more reactive elements form compounds more readily. Carbon's more reactive than iron, so carbon 'steals' oxygen from iron oxide (see page 35). It can also remove oxygen from zinc oxide and tin oxide.

3) In other words, carbon can only take the oxygen away from metals which are less reactive than carbon itself is.

4) Very reactive metals form very stable ores — i.e. it's difficult to get the metal out of its compound. So metals that are more reactive than carbon (they come higher in the reactivity series) have to be extracted using electrolysis. Electrolysis uses electricity to separate the metal from the other elements in the compound (see next page).

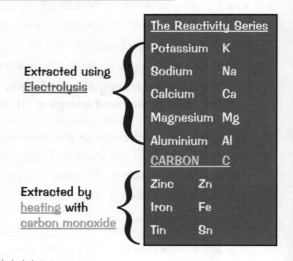

The Reactivity Series

Potassium	K
Sodium	Na
Calcium	Ca
Magnesium	Mg
Aluminium	Al
CARBON	C
Zinc	Zn
Iron	Fe
Tin	Sn

Extracted using Electrolysis

Extracted by heating with carbon monoxide

The reduction reaction using carbon is a bit like the displacement reactions with the halogens (see page 33).

Miners — they always have to stick their ore in...

Experiments can tell you where elements are in the reactivity series. For example, if you can extract a metal from its oxide by reacting it with carbon, then you know that the metal is less reactive than carbon. Simple as that.

Extracting Aluminium

As aluminium's more reactive than carbon, it has to be extracted from its ore using electrolysis...

Electrolysis Removes Aluminium from Its Ore

1) Aluminium's a very abundant metal, but it is always found naturally in compounds.
2) The main ore is bauxite, and after mining and purifying, a white powder is left.
3) This is pure aluminium oxide, Al_2O_3.

Cryolite is Used to Lower the Temperature (and Costs)

1) Al_2O_3 has a very high melting point of over 2000 °C — so melting it would be very expensive.
2) Instead the aluminium oxide is dissolved in molten cryolite (a less common ore of aluminium).
3) This brings the temperature down to about 900 °C, which makes it much cheaper and easier.
4) The electrodes are made of graphite, a good conductor of electricity.

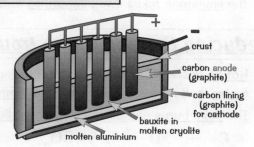

crust
carbon anode (graphite)
carbon lining (graphite) for cathode
bauxite in molten cryolite
molten aluminium

Electrolysis — Turning IONS into the ATOMS You Want

1) Molten aluminium oxide contains free ions — so it'll conduct electricity.
2) The positive Al^{3+} ions are attracted to the negative electrode (cathode) where they pick up electrons and "zup", they turn into aluminium atoms. These then sink to the bottom.
3) The negative O^{2-} ions are attracted to the positive electrode (anode) where they lose electrons. The oxygen atoms will then react together to form O_2, or with the carbon anode as well to form CO_2.
4) As the positive carbon electrode is constantly getting worn down by reacting with oxygen, it often needs replacing.

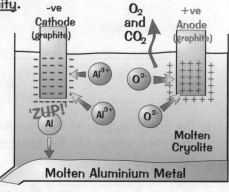

-ve Cathode (graphite)
O_2 and CO_2
+ve Anode (graphite)
'ZUP!' Al
Molten Cryolite
Molten Aluminium Metal

Overall, this is a REDOX reaction (reduction and oxidation both take place). You need to know the reactions at both electrodes:

At the negative electrode (cathode):	At the positive electrode (anode):
$$Al^{3+} + 3e^- \rightarrow Al$$	$$2O^{2-} \rightarrow O_2 + 4e^-$$
(Reduction — a gain of electrons)	(Oxidation — a loss of electrons)

The complete equation for the decomposition of aluminium oxide is then:

$$\text{aluminium oxide} \rightarrow \text{aluminium} + \text{oxygen}$$

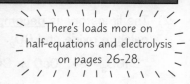
There's loads more on half-equations and electrolysis on pages 26-28.

Electrolysis is Expensive — It's All That Electricity...

1) Electrolysis uses a lot of electricity and that can make it pretty expensive.
2) Energy is also needed to heat the electrolyte mixture to 900 °C. This is expensive too.
3) The disappearing positive electrodes need frequent replacement. That costs money as well.
4) But in the end, aluminium now comes out as a reasonably cheap and widely-used metal. A hundred years ago it was a very rare metal, simply because it was so hard to extract.

What did the cheese say when it looked at itself in the mirror?...

Hallou mi... :) Now, you might think that that's got nothing to do with electrolysis, extracting aluminium or chemistry in general. And you'd be right. But a good cheese joke is, quite frankly, more fun. So why not, I say.

Extracting Iron

Iron is a very common element in the Earth's crust, but good iron ores are only found in a few select places around the world, such as Australia, Canada and Millom.
Iron is extracted from haematite, Fe_2O_3, by reduction (i.e. removal of oxygen) in a blast furnace.
You really do need to know all these details about what goes on in a blast furnace, including the equations.

The Raw Materials are Iron Ore, Coke and Limestone

1) The iron ore contains the iron — which is pretty important.

2) The coke is almost pure carbon. This is for reducing the iron oxide to iron metal.

3) The limestone takes away impurities in the form of slag.

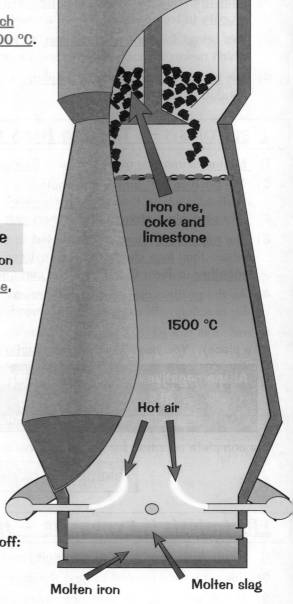

Iron ore, coke and limestone

1500 °C

Hot air

Molten iron   Molten slag

Reducing the Iron Ore to Iron:

1) Hot air is blasted into the furnace, making the coke burn much faster than normal. This raises the temperature to about 1500 °C.

2) The coke burns and produces carbon dioxide:

$$C + O_2 \rightarrow CO_2$$
carbon + oxygen → carbon dioxide

3) The CO_2 then reacts with unburnt coke to form CO:

$$CO_2 + C \rightarrow 2CO$$
carbon dioxide + carbon → carbon monoxide

4) The carbon monoxide then reduces the iron ore to iron:

$$3CO + Fe_2O_3 \rightarrow 3CO_2 + 2Fe$$
carbon monoxide + iron(III) oxide → carbon dioxide + iron

5) The iron is molten at this temperature and it's also very dense, so it runs straight to the bottom of the furnace where it's tapped off.

Removing the Impurities:

1) The main impurity is sand (silicon dioxide). This is still solid, even at 1500 °C, and would tend to stay mixed in with the iron. The limestone removes it.

2) The limestone is decomposed by the heat into calcium oxide and CO_2.

$$CaCO_3 \rightarrow CaO + CO_2$$

3) The calcium oxide then reacts with the sand to form calcium silicate, or slag, which is molten and can be tapped off:

$$CaO + SiO_2 \rightarrow CaSiO_3 \text{ (molten slag)}$$

4) The cooled slag is solid, and is used for:
   • Road-building   • Fertiliser

Learn the facts about iron extraction — it's a blast...

Three main sections and several numbered points for each. It's all important and could be tested in the exam, including the equations. Use the mini-essay method for each section. Or cover it up one section at a time, and try repeating the facts back to yourself. If you're in a public place people might think you're mad. But that's OK.

Uses of Iron and Aluminium

Iron and aluminium are the most produced metals in the whole wide world. So they often crop up in conversation, and you'll look really interesting if you know loads about them. OK, that's not true — but they do often come up in exams and right now that's probably a bit more relevant. So here's the info you'll need...

Iron and Aluminium have some Properties in Common

Both iron and aluminium have the same basic properties — they are both metals after all.

1) They are both dense and lustrous (i.e. shiny).
2) They have high melting points — iron melts at 1538 °C and aluminium melts at 660 °C.
3) They both have a high tensile strength — they're strong and hard to break.
4) But they can also be hammered into a different shape (they're malleable).
5) They are both good conductors of electricity...
6) ...and of heat energy too.

There's more on the properties of metals on page 25.

The Uses of Iron Depend on Its Properties...

Iron has all the properties you'd expect a metal to have. Adding other materials to the iron can change its properties though. This makes it really useful — different properties make it suitable for lots of different uses.

1) Wrought iron is almost completely pure iron. It's malleable, so it's used to make ornamental gates and railings.

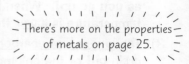

2) You can also mix iron with other elements to make alloys. These alloys have different properties to pure iron. For example:

- Cast iron is a mixture of iron, carbon and silicon. It's very hard, but brittle. Cast iron is used for manhole covers and some cooking pans.
- Steel is an alloy made of iron, carbon and (usually) some other metals. Steel has more useful properties than iron — e.g. it's harder than pure iron, but can still be hammered easily into sheets and welded together. These properties mean that steel is great for making car bodies and girders (for construction).

3) The main problem with iron is that it corrodes easily (i.e. it rusts).
4) Stainless steel is an alloy made of iron and chromium that doesn't rust. It's used for knives and forks and cooking pans. Makes sense — eating from a rusty fork doesn't really appeal...

...and so do the Uses of Aluminium

1) Aluminium is also a typical metal. However, unlike iron, it doesn't corrode easily.
2) The aluminium reacts very quickly with oxygen in the air to form aluminium oxide. A nice protective layer of aluminium oxide sticks firmly to the aluminium below and stops any further reaction taking place.
3) Because aluminium doesn't corrode it's useful for products that come in contact with water, e.g. drinks cans — you wouldn't want rust in your fizzy pop.
4) Aluminium is also much less dense than iron, which makes it lighter.
5) This makes it useful when the weight of the metal is important, e.g. in bicycle frames and aeroplanes.

What cheese do you use to hide a horse? Mask a pony...

Ha, I crack myself up. OK, sorry, enough with the cheese jokes — I'll get back to the chemistry. So, it's not just the main structures of aeroplanes that are made of aluminium — parts of the engines, the seat supports and even the trolleys are made of aluminium. Personally I find the cheese jokes more interesting, but whatever.

Fractional Distillation of Crude Oil

Over millions of years, high temperatures and pressures cause the buried remains of plants and animals to turn into crude oil. Then we come along, drill it up and burn it for energy — but this can produce pollutants.

Crude Oil is Separated into Different Hydrocarbon Fractions

Crude oil is a mixture of substances, most of which are hydrocarbons — molecules which are made of just carbon and hydrogen. The different compounds in crude oil are separated by fractional distillation:

1) The oil is heated until most of it has turned into gas. The gases enter a fractionating column (and the liquid bit, bitumen, is drained off at the bottom).

2) In the column there's a temperature gradient (i.e. it's hot at the bottom and gets gradually cooler as you go up). When the substances that make up crude oil reach a part of the column where the temperature is lower than their boiling point they condense (turn back into a liquid).

3) The longer hydrocarbons have high boiling points. They condense and drain out of the column early on, when they're near the bottom.

4) The shorter hydrocarbons have lower boiling points. They turn to liquid and drain out much later on, near to the top of the column where it's cooler.

5) Bubble caps in the fractionating column stop the separated liquids from running back down the column and remixing. You end up with the crude oil mixture separated out into different fractions. Each fraction contains a mixture of hydrocarbons with similar boiling points.

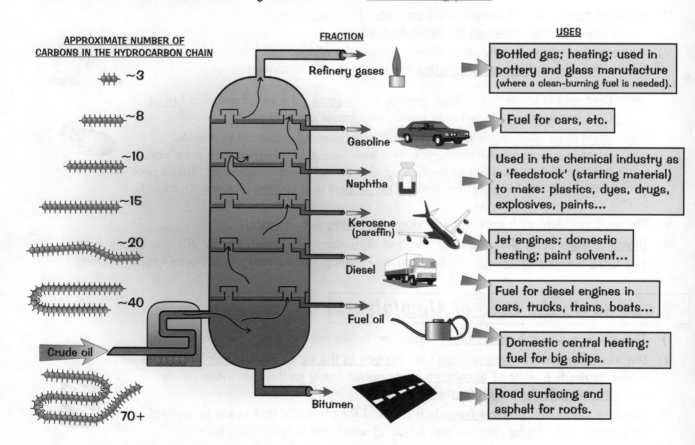

APPROXIMATE NUMBER OF CARBONS IN THE HYDROCARBON CHAIN

~3
~8
~10
~15
~20
~40
Crude oil
70+

FRACTION

Refinery gases

Gasoline

Naphtha

Kerosene (paraffin)

Diesel

Fuel oil

Bitumen

USES

Bottled gas; heating; used in pottery and glass manufacture (where a clean-burning fuel is needed).

Fuel for cars, etc.

Used in the chemical industry as a 'feedstock' (starting material) to make: plastics, dyes, drugs, explosives, paints...

Jet engines; domestic heating; paint solvent...

Fuel for diesel engines in cars, trucks, trains, boats...

Domestic central heating; fuel for big ships.

Road surfacing and asphalt for roofs.

Fractional distillation is an example of a physical process — there are no chemical reactions.

How much petrol is there in crude oil? Just a fraction...

Fractional distillation of crude oil is a favourite topic of chemistry examiners the world over, and it's not hard to see why when you look at what the products are. Gasoline (a.k.a. petrol), diesel and fuel oil are mighty useful chemicals, and we're pretty dependent on them at the moment. So you can't really blame the examiners for making you learn where they come from. Well, maybe you can, but you have to learn it anyway. Life's like that.

Pollutants

You don't have to be studying for a qualification in chemistry to know that burning fuel can produce pollution. But seeing as you <u>are</u> studying for a qualification in chemistry you'd best learn the details. Here they are...

Burning Fuels Can Produce Pollutants

A lot of the fractions obtained from crude oil are burnt as fuels. When they're burnt, pollutants such as carbon monoxide, nitrogen oxides and sulfur dioxide may be produced...

Carbon Monoxide is Produced by Incomplete Combustion

1) Carbon monoxide (CO) is formed when hydrocarbon fuels (e.g. petrol or diesel in car engines, or gas in central heating) are burnt without enough oxygen — this is incomplete combustion (see page 46).
2) Carbon monoxide is poisonous — it can stop your blood cells doing their proper job of carrying oxygen around the body. It combines with haemoglobin in blood cells, meaning the blood can carry less oxygen.
3) A lack of oxygen in the blood can lead to fainting, a coma or even death.

Sulfur Dioxide and Nitrogen Oxides Come from Burning Fuel

1) Sulfur dioxide (SO_2) and nitrogen oxides are also released when fossil fuels are burnt.
2) The sulfur dioxide comes from sulfur impurities in the fossil fuels.
3) Nitrogen oxides are created when the temperature is high enough for the nitrogen and oxygen in the air to react. This often happens in car engines. Nitrogen oxides include nitrogen monoxide (NO) and nitrogen dioxide (NO_2).

Acid Rain is Caused by Sulfur Dioxide and Nitrogen Oxides

1) All rain is slightly acidic because carbon dioxide in the air reacts with water to produce a slightly acidic solution.

$$CO_{2(g)} + H_2O_{(l)} \rightarrow H_2CO_{3(aq)}$$
carbon dioxide + water → carbonic acid

2) But when sulfur dioxide mixes with clouds it forms dilute sulfuric acid, which is much more acidic.
3) Nitrogen oxides can also form nitric acid in clouds.
4) The rain that falls from these clouds is called acid rain.

$$2SO_{2(g)} + O_{2(g)} + 2H_2O_{(l)} \rightarrow 2H_2SO_{4(aq)}$$
sulfur dioxide + oxygen + water → sulfuric acid

5) Acid rain causes lakes to become acidic and many plants and animals die as a result.
6) Acid rain kills trees and damages limestone buildings and ruins stone statues. It's shocking.
7) Links between acid rain and human health problems have been suggested.

A recent survey found that most trees now fear clouds... I don't blame 'em...

So, sulfur dioxide and nitrogen oxides cause acid rain, and carbon monoxide poisoning could even kill you. Bad news all round. How about a cheese joke to cheer you up? Yes? Excellent. Here goes... Did you hear about the explosion at the French cheese factory? All that was left was de brie. Ba-boom. Ah, how we laughed...

Cracking Hydrocarbons

The really long hydrocarbons aren't all that useful — but it's OK 'cause they can be made smaller by <u>cracking</u>.

Cracking — Splitting Up Long-Chain Hydrocarbons

1) <u>Long</u> hydrocarbons have <u>high</u> boiling points and are <u>viscous</u> (thick and gloopy).

2) <u>Shorter</u> hydrocarbons have <u>lower</u> boiling points and are much <u>thinner</u> and <u>paler</u> in colour.

3) Demand for <u>short-chain</u> hydrocarbons like octane, which is used in petrol, is much <u>higher</u> than for longer-chain hydrocarbons.

4) So, to <u>meet</u> this demand, long-chain hydrocarbons are <u>split</u> into <u>more useful</u> short-chain molecules using <u>cracking</u>.

5) <u>Cracking</u> is a form of <u>thermal decomposition</u>, which just means <u>breaking</u> molecules down into <u>simpler</u> molecules by <u>heating</u> them.

6) Cracking also produces <u>alkenes</u>, which are used to make <u>polymers</u> (see next page).

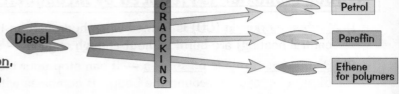

Conditions for Cracking: Heat, Plus a Catalyst

In industry, <u>vaporised hydrocarbons</u> are passed over a <u>powdered catalyst</u> at about <u>600 °C – 700 °C</u>. <u>Silica</u> (SiO_2) and <u>alumina</u> (Al_2O_3) are used as <u>catalysts</u>.

You can carry out the reaction in the lab using simple equipment. Like this...

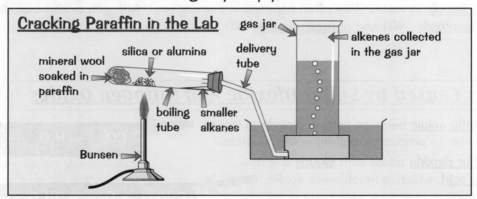

1) Start by <u>heating</u> the <u>paraffin</u>. After a few seconds, <u>move</u> the Bunsen burner to heat the <u>silica</u> or <u>alumina catalyst</u>. <u>Alternate</u> between the two until the paraffin <u>vaporises</u> and the catalyst <u>glows red</u>.

2) The heated paraffin vapour <u>cracks</u> as it passes over the heated catalyst.

3) <u>Small alkanes</u> collect at the end of the boiling tube, while <u>alkene gases</u> travel down the delivery tube.

4) The alkenes are then collected through <u>water</u> using a <u>gas jar</u>.

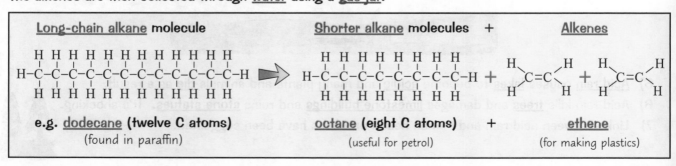

Bunsen and a boiling tube — cracking paraffin-alia...

So, cracking's useful for <u>two things</u> — making alkenes for plastics, and turning bitumen and candle wax (of limited use) into things like petrol and cooking gas (which are really rather handy). Definitely learn how viscosity and the boiling point change with hydrocarbon length too. Cover the page, scribble it all down, check, try again...

Addition Polymers

Plastics are formed when lots of small molecules called <u>monomers</u> join together to make a <u>polymer</u>. There are two basic types of polymer — <u>addition</u> (see below) and <u>condensation</u> (see next page).

Addition Polymers are Made Under High Pressure

The monomers that make up addition polymers have a <u>carbon-carbon double bond</u> — they're <u>alkenes</u> (see page 47).

Under <u>high pressure</u> and with a <u>catalyst</u> to help them along, many <u>small molecules</u> will open up those <u>double bonds</u> and 'join hands' (polymerise) to form <u>very long saturated chains</u> — <u>polymers</u>.

<u>Ethene</u> becoming <u>poly(ethene)</u> is the easiest example:

Polymers can be Shown Using Repeating Units

Addition polymerisation reactions can be written as an equation using <u>repeating units</u>. For example:

Poly(ethene)

The n here means there are lots of monomers.

Many single ethenes

The bit in brackets is the 'repeat unit'. n represents the number of repeat units.

Poly(propene)

Propene → Poly(propene)

Poly(chloroethene)

Chloroethene → Poly(chloroethene)

Paper 2

cm³ cm³ cm³ cm³ cm³ cm³ cm³ cm³ cm³

In the exam, you could be asked to <u>draw the repeat unit</u> of a polymer. You just have to find the section of polymer that's repeated and draw it out. For example:

This section of the polymer is repeated over and over again... ...so it must be the repeat unit.

The name of the polymer comes from the monomer it's made from — you just put brackets around the monomer and stick the word 'poly' in front of it.

To find the <u>monomer</u> used to form an addition polymer, take the repeat unit and <u>add a double bond</u>.

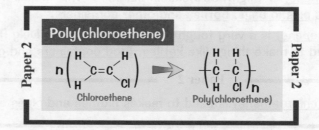

Repeat unit   Monomer

mol dm⁻³, mol dm⁻³, mol dm⁻³ mol dm⁻³, mol dm⁻³, mol dm⁻³...

There's so much plasticky goodness...

Plastics are dead useful. Everything from carrier bags to cars, bottles to school chairs are made from them. And all those plastics are made by joining together different types of <u>monomer</u> to make different types of <u>polymer</u>.

More on Polymers and Their Uses

Yep, more on polymers. Well, it's such a great topic, you wouldn't want just one page on it would you...
Well, OK, maybe you would, but the examiners have different ideas — so here's a second page.

Polymers can be Made by Condensation Polymerisation

1) Condensation polymerisation usually involves two different types of monomer.

2) The monomers react together and bonds form between them, making polymer chains.

3) For each new bond that forms, a small molecule (for example, water) is lost.

4) Nylon is an example of a condensation polymer.

| Monomer | Monomer | | Condensation polymer (nylon) | Water |

Polymers Have Lots of Uses

Different polymers have different physical properties, which makes them suitable for various different uses. For example:

1) Poly(ethene) is a light, stretchable polymer. This makes it ideal for making packaging such as plastic bags, bottles and other containers.

2) Poly(propene) is a very tough polymer, but it's relatively flexible and resistant to heat. It's used to make things like kettles, food containers and carpets.

Paper 2

3) Poly(chloroethene) is used to makes clothes and pipes and for insulating electrical cables.

Paper 2

Most Polymers are Hard to Get Rid Of

1) Most addition polymers are inert — they don't react easily. This is because the carbon-carbon bonds in the polymer chain are very strong and aren't easily broken.

2) This means that it takes a really long time for addition polymers to biodegrade (be broken down by bacteria or other organisms) — if you bury them in a landfill site, they'll still be there years later.

3) Burning plastics can release toxic gases, so that's not a great idea either.

4) So it's difficult to dispose of polymers. The best thing is to reuse them as many times as possible and then recycle them if you can.

Small water molecule — I release you...

So, addition polymers are formed when identical monomers are joined together in a polymer chain. Condensation polymers are made when different monomers react together. The only product of addition polymerisation is the polymer, but condensation polymerisation produces the polymer plus another small molecule. Got it? Fabuloso.

The Haber Process

This is an important industrial process. It produces ammonia (NH_3), which is used to make fertilisers.

Nitrogen and Hydrogen are Needed to Make Ammonia

$$N_2{}_{(g)} + 3H_2{}_{(g)} \rightleftharpoons 2NH_3{}_{(g)} \quad (+ \text{heat})$$

1) The nitrogen is obtained easily from the air, which is 78% nitrogen (and 21% oxygen).

2) The hydrogen comes from natural gas or from cracking hydrocarbons (see page 72).

3) Because the reaction is reversible (it occurs in both directions), not all of the nitrogen and hydrogen will convert to ammonia. The reaction reaches a dynamic equilibrium.

See page 64 for more on reversible reactions.

Industrial conditions: Pressure: 200 atmospheres; Temperature: 450 °C; Catalyst: Iron

The Reaction is Reversible, So There's a Compromise to be Made:

1) Higher pressures favour the forward reaction (since there are four molecules of gas on the left-hand side for every two molecules on the right).

2) So the pressure is set as high as possible to give the best % yield, without making the plant too expensive to build. Hence the 200 atmospheres operating pressure.

3) The forward reaction is exothermic, which means that increasing the temperature will actually move the equilibrium the wrong way — away from ammonia and towards N_2 and H_2. So the yield of ammonia would be greater at lower temperatures.

4) The trouble is, lower temperatures mean a slower rate of reaction (and so equilibrium is reached more slowly). So they increase the temperature anyway, to get a much faster rate of reaction.

5) The 450 °C is a compromise between maximum yield and speed of reaction. It's better to wait just 20 seconds for a 10% yield than to have to wait 60 seconds for a 20% yield.

6) The ammonia is formed as a gas, but as it cools in the condenser it liquefies and is removed. The unused hydrogen, H_2, and nitrogen, N_2, are recycled, so nothing is wasted.

7) The iron catalyst makes the reaction go faster, but doesn't affect the % yield.

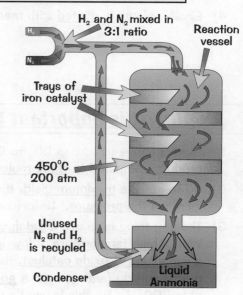

H_2 and N_2 mixed in 3:1 ratio

Reaction vessel

Trays of iron catalyst

450°C 200 atm

Unused N_2 and H_2 is recycled

Condenser

Liquid Ammonia

Ammonia is Used to Make Nitric Acid and Ammonium Nitrate Fertiliser

1) Ammonia is used in the Ostwald process to make nitric acid (HNO_3).

2) You can also react ammonia with nitric acid, to get ammonium nitrate. Ammonium nitrate is an especially good fertiliser because it has nitrogen from two sources, the ammonia and the nitric acid. Kind of a double dose. Plants need nitrogen to make proteins.

3) Ammonium nitrate is a much more effective fertiliser than organic alternatives (e.g. pig poo), so it helps farmers produce crops from land that otherwise wouldn't have been fertile enough.

You need to learn this stuff — go on, Haber go at it...

The trickiest bit is remembering that the temperature is raised not for a better equilibrium, but for speed. Cover the page and scribble down as much as you can remember, then check, and try again.

The Contact Process

The contact process. 'What the heck is that...', you say. Well, it's dead good. It really is something special. In fact, it's so good I don't want to ruin the surprise by giving you any clues to what it's about here. So there are no spoilers in this intro — you can read the page and discover its wondrous-ness all by yourself.

The Contact Process is Used to Make Sulfuric Acid

1) The first stage of the contact process involves forming sulfur dioxide (SO_2) gas. This is usually done by burning sulfur in air or roasting sulfide ores.

$$S + O_2 \rightarrow SO_2$$

2) The sulfur dioxide is then oxidised (with the help of a catalyst) to form sulfur trioxide (SO_3) gas.

$$2SO_2 + O_2 \rightleftharpoons 2SO_3$$

3) Next, the sulfur trioxide is dissolved in concentrated sulfuric acid to form liquid oleum.

$$SO_3 + H_2SO_4 \rightarrow H_2S_2O_7$$

4) Finally, oleum is diluted with measured amounts of water to form concentrated sulfuric acid.

$$H_2S_2O_7 + H_2O \rightarrow 2H_2SO_4$$

A Catalyst is Important When Making SO_3

1) Step 2 above (oxidising SO_2 to SO_3) is exothermic (it gives out heat). Also, there are two moles of product compared to three moles of reactants (so the product has less volume than the reactants).

2) So to get the maximum yield, the obvious thing to do would be to reduce the temperature and increase the pressure. Unfortunately, reducing the temperature slows the reaction right down.

3) The key thing is to use a catalyst...
With a high temperature, a low-ish pressure and a vanadium(V) oxide catalyst, the reaction goes pretty quickly (and you get a good yield — about 99%). So this is what's done in practice.

Conditions for Contact Process
1) Temperature: 450 °C.
2) Pressure: 2 atmospheres.
3) Catalyst: Vanadium(V) oxide, V_2O_5.

Modern Industry Uses Loads of Sulfuric Acid

Sulfuric acid is used in many manufacturing processes.
For example, it's used to make:

- Fertilisers — sulfuric acid is mostly used to make phosphate fertilisers. Farmers use them to improve the amount of nutrients in the soil — this increases plant growth.

- Detergents — used for cleaning just about anything and everything.

- Paints — sulfuric acid is used to make titanium dioxide, which is a white pigment that's used in paints (and for drawing white lines on tennis courts).

The contact process — it's a touching story...

Yep, all that stuff about the contact process being wondrous was a BIG FAT LIE. But you probably didn't believe me anyway, so I won't beat myself up about it. Anyways, making SO_3 is the key thing in the contact process (but do learn the other stages too). Then all that's left to learn are the various uses of sulfuric acid. Easy.

Electrolysis of Brine

Electrolysis of brine (sodium chloride solution) was covered briefly in Section 1 on page 27.
This page goes into a bit more <u>detail</u>, and yes, you do need to know the details. Sorry 'bout that.

Electrolysis of Salt gives Hydrogen, Chlorine and NaOH

<u>Concentrated brine</u> (sodium chloride solution) is <u>electrolysed</u> industrially using a <u>diaphragm cell</u>
a bit like this one. It produces <u>three</u> useful products:

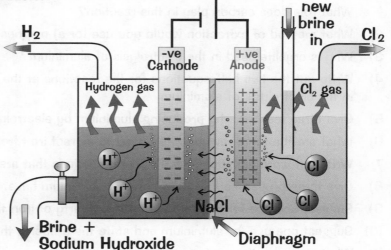

- <u>Hydrogen gas</u> is given off at the cathode — two hydrogen ions accept two electrons to become <u>one hydrogen molecule</u>.

- <u>Chlorine gas</u> is given off at the anode — two chloride ions (Cl⁻) lose their electrons and become <u>one chlorine molecule</u>.

- The <u>sodium ions</u> (Na⁺) stay in solution and the <u>hydroxide ions</u> (OH⁻) from the water are also left behind. This means that <u>sodium hydroxide</u> is left in the <u>solution</u>.

The Half-Equations — Make Sure the Electrons Balance

You can write out <u>half-equations</u> for the reactions that take place at the <u>anode</u> and the <u>cathode</u>.
The main thing is to make sure the <u>number of electrons</u> is the <u>same</u> for <u>both half-equations</u>.
For the electrolysis of sodium chloride the half-equations are:

<u>Cathode:</u> $2H^+ + 2e^- \rightarrow H_2$
<u>Anode:</u> $2Cl^- \rightarrow Cl_2 + 2e^-$

There's more about half-equations on page 26.

Useful Products from the Electrolysis of Brine

With all that effort and expense going into the electrolysis of brine, there'd better be some pretty useful
stuff coming out of it — and so there is... and you have to learn it all too. Ace.

1) Chlorine

Chlorine is used to <u>sterilise water supplies</u> (chlorination). It's also used to make <u>bleach</u> and <u>HCl</u>.

2) Hydrogen

Hydrogen is used in the <u>Haber process</u> and to change <u>oils</u> into <u>fats</u> for making <u>margarine</u>.

3) Sodium Hydroxide

Sodium hydroxide is a very strong <u>base</u> and is used <u>widely</u> in the <u>chemical industry</u>.
For example, it's used to make <u>soap</u>, <u>bleach</u> and <u>paper pulp</u>.

Brine? He's not the Messiah — he's a very naughty boy...

The industrial electrolysis of brine started as a way to make <u>sodium hydroxide</u> and used mercury as one of the
electrodes. But this caused big environmental problems, so cells like the diaphragm cell above are used today.

Revision Summary for Section 5

It's the end of the last section, woooo. And what a section — full of industrial-sized processes and reactions that are going to take an industrial amount of learning to remember. But don't panic, because I have just the thing to help you on your way — it's the revision summary. Keep going through the questions until you can get all the answers without having to look back at the section and you'll soon get that industrial-sized mark.

1) Are metal oxides reduced or oxidised to obtain the metal from them?
   What role does carbon play in this reaction?

2) What method of extraction would you use for a) magnesium, b) iron?

3) Why is cryolite used in the electrolysis of aluminium?

4) Write out the two half-equations for the reactions at the anode and the cathode in the electrolysis of aluminium.

5) Give three reasons why producing aluminium by electrolysis is expensive.

6) What are the three raw materials used to extract iron from its ore?

7) Write out word equations for the three reactions that are used to extract iron.

8) Give three properties that both iron and aluminium have.

9) Suggest one use for iron and state the property of iron that makes it suitable for that use.

10) Suggest one use for aluminium and state the property that makes it suitable for that use.

11) What is crude oil a mixture of?

12) Describe how fractional distillation is used to separate crude oil into fractions.

13) Name five fractions of crude oil and what they're used for.

14) Explain how nitrogen oxides are formed from burning fuels. Where is this likely to happen?

15) What conditions are needed for the production of carbon monoxide when a fuel is burnt?

16) Why is carbon monoxide poisonous?

17) How do the boiling points of hydrocarbons change as the chain length gets longer?

18) What is cracking? Why do we need to crack hydrocarbons?

19) What are the conditions used to crack a hydrocarbon industrially?

20) What kind of polymers are made from monomers with a carbon-carbon double bond?

21) Draw the repeat unit for this polymer.

$$-\overset{\displaystyle H}{\underset{\displaystyle H}{C}}-\overset{\displaystyle H}{\underset{\displaystyle Cl}{C}}-\overset{\displaystyle H}{\underset{\displaystyle H}{C}}-\overset{\displaystyle H}{\underset{\displaystyle Cl}{C}}-\overset{\displaystyle H}{\underset{\displaystyle H}{C}}-\overset{\displaystyle H}{\underset{\displaystyle Cl}{C}}-$$

22) What kind of polymers are made when a small molecule is released during the reaction?

23) Give one use for poly(ethene).

24) Write out the reaction that takes place in the Haber process.

25) What are the industrial conditions used in the Haber process?

26) Give two uses for the ammonia that's produced in the Haber process.

27) What does the contact process produce?

28) What are the industrial conditions used for the contact process?

29) Sketch a picture of a diaphragm cell that is used to electrolyse brine. Label the anode, cathode, diaphragm, where the brine enters the cell and where the products leave the cell.

30) Write out the half-equations that take place at the anode and the cathode when brine is electrolysed.

31) Give two uses of chlorine and two uses of sodium hydroxide.

Experimental Know-How

Real scientists need to know how to plan and carry out scientific experiments. Unluckily for you, those pesky examiners think you should be able to do the same — that's why up to 25% of your marks will come from questions that test your experimental know-how. Don't worry though — that's what this section's all about.

You Might Get Asked Questions on Reliability and Validity

1) RELIABLE results come from experiments that give the same data:

- each time the experiment is repeated (by you),
- each time the experiment is reproduced by other scientists.

2) VALID results are both reliable AND come from experiments that were designed to be a fair test.

In the exam, you could be asked to suggest ways to improve the reliability or validity of some experimental results. If so, there are a couple of things to think about:

1 Controlling Variables Improves Validity

1) A variable is something that has the potential to change, e.g. temperature. In a lab experiment you usually change one variable and measure how it affects another variable.

EXAMPLE: you might change only the temperature of a chemical reaction and measure how this affects the rate of reaction.

2) To make it a fair test, everything else that could affect the results should stay the same — otherwise you can't tell if the thing you're changing is causing the results or not.

EXAMPLE continued: you need to keep the concentration of the reactants the same, otherwise you won't know if any change in the rate of reaction is caused by the change in temperature, or a difference in reactant concentration.

3) The variable you CHANGE is called the INDEPENDENT variable.
4) The variable you MEASURE is called the DEPENDENT variable.
5) The variables that you KEEP THE SAME are called CONTROL variables.

EXAMPLE continued:
Independent variable = temperature
Dependent variable = rate of reaction
Control variables = concentration of reactants, volume/mass of reactants, etc.

6) Because you can't always control all the variables, you often need to use a CONTROL EXPERIMENT — an experiment that's kept under the same conditions as the rest of the investigation, but doesn't have anything done to it. This is so that you can see what happens when you don't change anything at all.

2 Carrying Out Repeats Improves Reliability

1) To improve reliability you need to repeat any measurements you make and calculate the mean (average).
2) You need to repeat each measurement at least three times.

Reliable results — they won't ever forget your birthday...

A typical exam question might describe an experiment, then ask you to suggest what variables need to be controlled. Don't panic, just use your scientific knowledge and a bit of common sense, e.g. if the experiment involves paper chromatography, you know that it's affected by the solvent and the paper you use, so these variables need to be kept constant (providing you're not actually investigating one of them). You might also need to say how you'd control the variables, e.g. the temperature of a reaction could be controlled using a water bath.

Experimental Know-How

Thought you knew <u>everything</u> there was to know about experiments? <u>Think again</u> my friend...

You Might Have to *Suggest Ways to Make an Experiment Safer*

1) It's important that experiments are safe. If you're asked to suggest ways to make an experiment safer, you'll first need to identify what the <u>potential hazards</u> might be. Hazards include things like:

Hmm... Where did my acid go?

- <u>Chemicals</u>, e.g. sulfuric acid can burn your skin and alcohols catch fire easily.
- <u>Fire</u>, e.g. an unattended Bunsen burner is a fire hazard.
- <u>Electricity</u>, e.g. faulty electrical equipment could give you a shock.

2) Then you'll need to suggest ways of <u>reducing</u> the <u>risks</u> involved with the hazard, e.g.

- If you're working with <u>sulfuric acid</u>, always wear gloves and safety goggles. This will reduce the risk of the acid coming into contact with your skin and eyes.
- If you're using a <u>Bunsen burner</u>, stand it on a heat proof mat. This will reduce the risk of starting a fire.
- If you're working with <u>chemicals</u> that give off <u>harmful gases</u>, you need to use a fume cupboard. This will reduce the risk of you breathing in the gases.

You Could be Asked About Accuracy...

1) It's important that results are **ACCURATE**. Really accurate results are those that are <u>really close</u> to the <u>true answer</u>.
2) The accuracy of your results usually depends on your <u>method</u>.

E.g. say you wanted to measure the <u>rate</u> of a <u>chemical reaction</u> that releases a <u>gas</u> as a product. The rate of the reaction would be the <u>amount of gas produced per unit time</u>. You could <u>estimate</u> how much gas is produced by <u>counting</u> the number of <u>bubbles</u> that are released. But the bubbles could be <u>different sizes</u>, and if they're produced really quickly you might <u>miss some</u> when counting. It would be more accurate to <u>collect the gas</u> (e.g. using a gas syringe) and <u>measure</u> its <u>volume</u>.

3) To make sure your results are as <u>accurate</u> as possible, you need to make sure you're measuring the <u>right thing</u> and that you <u>don't miss</u> anything or <u>include</u> anything that shouldn't be included in the measurements.

E.g. if you're measuring the volume of gas produced using a gas syringe, you need to make sure the syringe is <u>empty</u> at the start of the experiment. If there's any air in it the reading will be <u>wrong</u>.

...And Precision

1) Results also need to be <u>PRECISE</u>. Precise results are those taken using <u>sensitive instruments</u> that measure in <u>small increments</u>, e.g. using a ruler with a millimetre scale gives more precise data than using a ruler with a scale in centimetres.
2) By recording your results to a <u>greater number</u> of <u>decimal places</u>, you'll increase their precision, e.g.

In some exam questions, you'll be told how precise to be in your answer. So if you're told to give an answer to 2 decimal places, make sure you do or you could lose marks.

Repeat	Data set 1	Data set 2
1	12	11.98
2	14	14.00
3	13	13.01

The results in data set 2 are more precise than those in data set 1.

Safety first — goggles on before you read this book...

It may interest you to know that you won't just have to write about other people's experiments in the exam. Sometimes you'll be asked to <u>describe</u> how you'd carry out your <u>own experiment</u> and all this stuff about reliability and what not will apply then too. Ah. From the look on your face, I'm guessing it didn't interest you to know that.

Drawing Graphs and Interpreting Results

If you're presented with some results from an experiment you've got to know <u>what to do with them</u>.

You Should Be Able to Identify Anomalous Results

1) Most results vary a bit, but any that are <u>totally different</u> are called <u>anomalous results</u>.
2) They're <u>caused</u> by <u>human errors</u>, e.g. by a mistake made when measuring or by not setting up a piece of equipment properly.
3) You could be asked to <u>identify</u> an anomalous result in the exam and suggest what <u>caused</u> it — just look for a result that <u>doesn't fit in</u> with the rest (e.g. it's <u>too high</u> or <u>too low</u>) then try to figure out what could have <u>gone wrong</u> with the experiment to have caused it.
4) If you're calculating an <u>average</u>, you can <u>ignore</u> any anomalous results.

You Need to Be Able to Draw Graphs...

In the exam, you might be asked to draw a <u>graph</u> or <u>bar chart</u> from a set of results.
If you're not told which one to go for, here's how you decide:

1) If the independent variable is <u>categoric</u> (comes in distinct categories, e.g. ion charge, metals) you should use a <u>bar chart</u> to display the data.
2) If the independent variable is <u>continuous</u> (can take any value within a range, e.g. length, volume, time) you should use a <u>line graph</u> to display the data.

Here are a few useful tips for <u>drawing line graphs</u>:

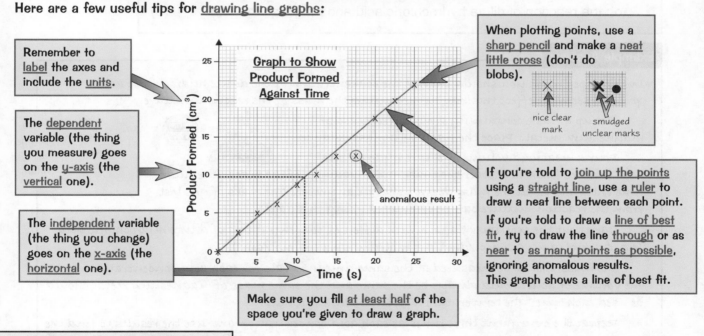

When plotting points, use a <u>sharp pencil</u> and make a <u>neat little cross</u> (don't do blobs).

nice clear mark

smudged unclear marks

Remember to <u>label</u> the axes and include the <u>units</u>.

The <u>dependent</u> variable (the thing you measure) goes on the <u>y-axis</u> (the <u>vertical</u> one).

The <u>independent</u> variable (the thing you change) goes on the <u>x-axis</u> (the <u>horizontal</u> one).

anomalous result

If you're told to <u>join up the points</u> using a <u>straight line</u>, use a <u>ruler</u> to draw a neat line between each point.

If you're told to draw a <u>line of best fit</u>, try to draw the line <u>through</u> or as <u>near</u> to <u>as many points as possible</u>, ignoring anomalous results. This graph shows a line of best fit.

Make sure you fill <u>at least half</u> of the space you're given to draw a graph.

...And Interpret Them

1) A graph is used to show the <u>relationship</u> between two variables — you need to be able to look at a graph and <u>describe</u> this relationship. For example, the graph above shows that as <u>time goes on</u>, <u>more product is formed</u>.
2) You also need to be able to <u>read information</u> off a graph. In this example, if you wanted to know how much product had been formed by <u>11 s</u>, you'd draw a <u>vertical line up</u> from the x-axis at 11 s and a <u>horizontal line across</u> to the y-axis. This would tell you that the amount of product formed by 11 s was around <u>9.7 cm³</u>.

As rate of revision increases, so does boredom...

It's not just graphs you'll have to deal with in the exam, it's <u>tables</u> too. For example, you might be asked to describe the results in a table or pick out an anomalous result. You'll also be expected to do a bit of <u>basic maths</u>, like <u>calculating</u> a <u>mean</u> (add everything together and divide by the total number of values) or a <u>percentage</u>.

Planning Experiments and Evaluating Conclusions

In the exam, you could be asked to plan or describe how you'd carry out an experiment. The experiment might be one you've already come across (easy) or (gasp) you might be asked to come up with an experiment of your own to test something. You might also be asked to say what you think of someone else's conclusion. I know. Examiners are harsh. It's not as bad as it sounds though.

You Need to Be Able to Plan a Good Experiment

Here are some general tips on what to include when planning an experiment:

1) Say what you're measuring (i.e. what the dependent variable is going to be).

2) Say what you're changing (i.e. what the independent variable is going to be) and describe how you're going to change it.

3) Describe the method and the apparatus you'd use.

4) Describe what variables you're keeping constant — and how you're going to do it.

5) Say that you need to repeat the experiment at least three times, to make the results more reliable.

6) Say whether you're using a control or not.

Here's an idea of the sort of thing you might be asked in the exam and what you might write as an answer...

Exam-style Question:

1   Describe an experiment to investigate the effect of concentration on the reaction of dilute hydrochloric acid and magnesium metal.   (6)

Example Answer:

In this experiment you should change the concentration of the dilute hydrochloric acid. You can see what effect this has by measuring the mass of the reaction mixture.

Set up a flask containing a measured mass of magnesium metal. Place the flask on a mass balance.

Pour a measured volume of dilute hydrochloric acid into the flask and start the timer. Take readings of the mass at regular time intervals until the mass doesn't change anymore. The mass of gas lost from the reaction mixture can be calculated using this data.

Carry out the experiment again with different concentrations of dilute hydrochloric acid (e.g. 0.1 mol/dm³, 0.2 mol/dm³, 0.3 mol/dm³ and 0.4 mol/dm³).

The mass should be measured at the same time intervals for each acid concentration. The volume of acid should always be the same and the same mass of magnesium metal should be used each time. The temperature must also remain constant.

Repeat the experiment three times at each acid concentration and use the results to find the average mass of gas lost at each time interval for each concentration.

> You could also collect the hydrogen in a gas syringe and measure its volume.

You Could Be Asked to Evaluate a Conclusion

1) In the exam, you could be given an experimental conclusion and asked to evaluate it.

2) This just means saying whether or not you think evidence from the experiment supports the conclusion — and why.

Plan your way to exam success...

The number of marks available for a question like this will vary, but it'll usually be around five or six. This means you'll have to write an extended answer. Think about what you're going to say beforehand and in what order — that way you're less likely to forget something important. Like what it is you're actually measuring, say.

Index

Answers

Revision Summary for Section 1 — 1 (page 15)

10) a) 3   b) 2   c) 1   d) 4

11) a) crystallisation   b) fractional distillation   c) filtration

16) 2, 8, 8, 1

Bottom of page 16

1) $Fe_2O_3 + 3H_2 \rightarrow 2Fe + 3H_2O$

2) $6HCl + 2Al \rightarrow 2AlCl_3 + 3H_2$

Bottom of page 18

NaOH: 40

Fe_2O_3: 160

C_6H_{14}: 86

$Mg(NO_3)_2$: 148

Bottom of page 19

C	H
2.4	0.8
$2.4 \div 12 = 0.2$	$0.8 \div 1 = 0.8$
2	8
1	4

So the empirical formula is CH_4.

Bottom of page 20

1) $2Ca + O_2 \rightarrow 2CaO$
$M_r\ 2Ca = 2 \times 40 = 80$
$M_r\ 2CaO = (40 + 16) \times 2 = 112$

2Ca	2CaO
80 g	112 g
0.714 g	1 g
21.4 g	30 g

2) $2K + F_2 \rightarrow 2KF$
$M_r\ F_2 = 19 \times 2 = 38$
$M_r\ 2KF = 2 \times (39 + 19) = 116$

F_2	2KF
38 g	116 g

Revision Summary for Section 1 — 2 (page 29)

2) a) $2Na + 2H_2O \rightarrow 2NaOH + H_2$

b) $2Al + 6HCl \rightarrow 2AlCl_3 + 3H_2$

4) 20.18

5) a) 98   b) 125   c) 82   d) 72

6) Ca: $227 \div 40 = 5.68$
F: $216 \div 19 = 11.37$
Divide both by 5.68 to get a ratio of 1:2.
So, the empirical formula is CaF_2.

7) empirical mass $= (2 \times 12) + (5 \times 1) + 35.5 = 64.5$
number of empirical units in the molecule
$= 258 \div 64.5 = 4$ empirical units
$C_2H_5Cl \times 4 = C_8H_{20}Cl_4$

8) a) $4Na + O_2 \rightarrow 2Na_2O$
$4Na: 4 \times 23 = 92$
$2Na_2O: ((23 \times 2) + 16) \times 2) = 124$

Na	Na_2O
92 g	124 g
1 g	1.348 g
50 g	67.4 g (to 1 d.p.)

b) Percentage yield $= 42.3 \div 67.4 \times 100 = 62.8\%$ (to 1 d.p.)

9) moles $= $ mass $\div M_r = 147 \div (23 + 16 + 1)$
$= 147 \div 40 = 3.7$ moles (to 1 d.p.)

10) mass $= $ moles $\times M_r = 0.05 \times (24 + 16)$
$= 0.05 \times 40 = 2$ g

11) mass of $FeCl_2.XH_2O = 28.133 - 23.299 = 4.834$ g
mass of $FeCl_2 = 26.347 - 23.299 = 3.048$ g
mass of H_2O lost $= 4.834 - 3.048 = 1.786$ g
moles H_2O lost $= 1.786 \div 18 = 0.0992$
M_r of $FeCl_2 = 56 + (35.5 \times 2) = 127$ g/mol
moles of $FeCl_2$ in 3.048 g $= 3.048$ g $\div 127$ g/mol $= 0.024$ mole
$X = 0.0992 \div 0.024 = 4.13 \approx 4$
So, the formula of the hydrated salt is $FeCl_2.4H_2O$.

12) volume $= $ moles $\times 24 = 88.8\ dm^3$

13) moles $= $ concentration $\times$ volume
$= 2 \times (250 \div 1000) = 0.5$ moles

14) concentration $= $ moles $\div$ volume
$= 0.55 \div (500 \div 1000)$
$= 0.55 \div 0.5 = 1.1\ mol/dm^3$

21) $Pb^{2+} + 2e^- \rightarrow Pb$
charge $= $ current $\times$ time $= 7200$ C
faradays $= 7200 \div 96\ 000 = 0.075$ F
moles of product $= 0.075 \div 2$ (electrons)
$= 0.0375$ moles of Pb atoms
mass Pb $= M_r \times$ moles $= 207 \times 0.0375 = 7.76$ g (to 2 d.p)

Revision Summary for Section 2 (page 44)

18) Magnesium displaces copper to form magnesium oxide.

19) The aluminium will displace the zinc to form aluminium sulfate.

Revision Summary for Section 4 (page 65)

4) $2HCl + ZnCO_3 \rightarrow ZnCl_2 + H_2O + CO_2$

8) Number of moles of NaOH
$= $ concentration $\times$ volume $= 0.25 \times (25/1000) = 0.00625$
Equation: $NaOH + HCl \rightarrow NaCl + H_2O$
There's one mole of NaOH to every mole of HCl,
so 0.00625 moles of HCl were used.
Concentration of HCl
$= 0.00625 \div (42/1000) = 0.15$ moles per dm^3

11) b)

17) a) Bonds broken:
2 moles of H–H bonds $= 2 \times 436 = 872$ kJ
1 mole of O=O bonds $= 496$ kJ
Total energy needed to break bonds $= 872 + 496 = 1368$ kJ
Bonds made:
2 moles of (2 × O–H bonds) $= 2 \times 2 \times 463 = 1852$ kJ
So enthalpy change ($\triangle H$) $= 1368 - 1852 = -484$ kJ/mol.

b) This is an exothermic reaction.

18) a) Mass of water heated $= 116$ g $- 64$ g $= 52$ g
Temperature rise of water $= 47\ ^\circ C - 17\ ^\circ C = 30\ ^\circ C$
Mass of pentane burnt $= 97.72$ g $- 97.37$ g $= 0.35$ g
So 0.35 g of pentane provides enough energy to heat up 52 g of water by 30 °C.
It takes 4.2 joules of energy to heat up 1 g of water by 1 °C.
Therefore, the energy produced in this experiment is $4.2 \times 52 \times 30 = 6552$ joules.
So, 0.35 g of pentane produces 6552 joules of energy, meaning 1 g of pentane produces 6552/0.35 = 18 720 J or 18.72 kJ